5

7

CAN I — CAN I THINK ABOUT IT?

OF COURSE. BUT DON'T TAKE TOO LONG. I'M OFF TO THE STATES SOON TO DO SOME PROMOTIONAL WORK. YOU COULD COME WITH ME.

EVERYTHING'S HAPPENED TOO QUICKLY. CHLOE MAY BE READY TO HAVE ME BACK BUT I'M NOT READY TO GO. I LIKE CHLOE, BUT I *LOVE* MY FOSTER MUM AND DAD. AND I COULD *NEVER* LEAVE JOE.

Claire told her mum, and —

WHAT DID SHE SAY? WAS SHE ANNOYED I WOULDN'T GO WITH HER?

NO, SHE JUST SOUNDED SURPRISED. I THINK SHE THOUGHT YOU'D JUMP AT THE CHANCE OF LIVING WITH HER.

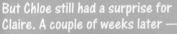

But Chloe still had a surprise for Claire. A couple of weeks later —

GUESS WHAT? CHLOE'S FINALLY AGREED TO LET US ADOPT CLAIRE. NOW THERE'S NOTHING TO STOP US FROM BEING ONE HAPPY FAMILY.

BUT WE WERE THAT ANYWAY, MUM. THAT'S WHY I DIDN'T WANT TO LEAVE.

IT'S STILL MY GO ON THE COMPUTER, SIS!

NO WAY! YOU WERE ON IT LAST TIME!

SO WE'RE BACK TO NORMAL — THANK GOODNESS!

THE END

Make...make...make...

Next time your mates come round to watch a video – or just have a natter – forget the crisps! We show you how to make some simple snacks that'll turn the evening into a party! Have fun!

Cool-kebabs

Ingredients:
Selection of small or chopped vegetables
Cocktail sausages
Tomato ketchup
Cocktail sticks

Method:
Thread a mixture of vegetables on to each cocktail stick and top with a mini sausage. Dip each kebab into the ketchup and eat! Munchsome!
For something **really** special, you can make cool **fruit** kebabs. Use chunks of your fave fruits and dip them in yoghurt or creme fraiche.

Tuna-treats

Ingredients:
Two wide sticks of celery
A small tin of tuna
Mayonnaise
A little chopped red pepper
to garnish
Toasted bread
Seasoning to taste

Method:
Drain the tuna and mix it with mayonnaise and seasoning to taste. Cut the celery into equal lengths (around 8cm is ideal) and pile the tuna mixture inside. You can turn your Tuna-treats into boats by using a cocktail stick to fix a small triangle of toast on top. Garnish with pieces of chopped red pepper. Crunchable!

Choccie-chomps

Ingredients:
Chocolate
Fruits and nuts

Method:
Prepare your fruit by cutting or separating it into small sections. Melt the chocolate, either in a bowl over some boiling water or in the microwave. One by one, carefully dip the pieces of fruit or nuts halfway into the melted chocolate and leave to dry on a sheet of waxed paper. Mmmmm!

Mini-mouthfuls

Ingredients:
Bread
Spread
Filling
A little oil for frying

Method:
Make the sandwiches as usual, filling them with your favourite sarnie stuffing. Remove the crusts and cut the sandwiches into small pieces. Fry lightly until golden on each side. Scrummy! Try serving the toasts with a dip such as humous or mayonnaise.

Rockin' rolls

Ingredients:
Raw vegetables
Sliced ham

Method:
Cut your favourite vegetables into the shape of short chips. Slice a piece of ham into two and then roll each strip round a vegetable chip. Simplicity!

ALWAYS ASK PERMISSION FROM AN ADULT BEFORE WORKING OR COOKING IN THE KITCHEN.

IS FASHION YOUR PASSION?

Follow our fun flow **START** ▷ **DO YOU LIKE TO EXPERIMENT WITH YOUR HAIR AND MAKE UP?**
chart and find out.

DO YOU HAVE TO HAVE THE LATEST LOOK?

DO YOU CUSTOMISE YOUR CLOTHES OR UNIFORM?

WOULD YOU LIKE TO LOOK LIKE YOUR FAVE POP STAR?

DO YOU LIKE TO CHANGE YOUR LOOK OFTEN?

DO YOU CHECK THE FASHION PAGES FIRST IN MAGAZINES?

YOU'LL ONLY WEAR THINGS WHICH SUIT YOU. TRUE?

DO YOU SPEND ALL YOUR POCKET MONEY ON LOOKING GOOD?

DO YOU OWN LOTS OF SHOES?

YOU LOVE PAINTING YOUR TOENAILS. TRUE?

YOU FIND A LOOK YOU LIKE AND STICK WITH IT? TRUE?

DO YOUR FRIENDS THINK YOU'RE TRENDY?

ARE YOU QUICKLY BORED WITH CLOTHES YOU BUY?

YOU'D LOVE TO BE A FASHION DESIGNER. TRUE?

LOOKING GOOD'S MORE IMPORTANT THAN COMFORT. TRUE?

You like fashion but it doesn't rule your life. You look around, choose what suits you, and always look good. Friends will often ask your opinion on what to buy.

You're a true fashion victim - you love getting the latest looks, wearing them, then looking out for the next craze. Friends are always amazed by your new looks.

You're not into fashion at all. You wear clothes that you've had for years and go looking for clothes only when you have to. You're always far too busy with other things.

schools cool!

12 reasons why we lurve school!

and 5 reasons why we're not so keen.

School dinners!

Bullies!

Teachers!

Exams!

Uniforms!

We get to meet our mates and have a good gossip!

We learn lots of interesting things!

It gets us away from our bothersome big/little brother or sister!

Homework is a good excuse for avoiding chores. "Sorry, Mum. I can't wash the dishes cos I've got loads of homework to do!"

There are lots of tasty lads to eye up – unless you go to an all girls school, that is!

If we do well, we can win prizes. If we don't we can say that only swots win prizes!

School parties and outings are cool!

We can listen to our favourite music in music class – sometimes!

We get to use computers without Mum or Dad wanting a turn!

We can splash paint around in art class and claim we're being creative!

Playtime!

Hometime!

SCHOOL RULES! **The Comp**

IT was almost holiday time at Redvale Comp —

JUST A MOMENT, BECKY. CAN I HAVE A WORD?

OH-OH! WHAT'S MY TWIN SIS BEEN UP TO NOW?

IT'LL BE NO GOOD! THAT'S FOR CERTAIN.

YOU'VE BEEN HANDING IN SOME GOOD WORK THIS TERM, BECKY, SO I THOUGHT YOU MIGHT BE INTERESTED IN THIS.

THANKS, MISS TRACY. WHAT IS IT?

IT'S A SCHOOL TRIP THAT THE ART DEPARTMENT HAS ARRANGED FOR THE LAST WEEK OF TERM, VISITING GALLERIES IN PARIS. ARE YOU INTERESTED?

YOU BET! BUT — BUT HOW MUCH IS IT?

IT'S PROBABLY WAY OUT OF OUR BUDGET.

THAT'S THE REALLY GOOD THING. WE'RE PAYING COSTS FOR PUPILS WE THINK SHOW REAL TALENT. SO, IF YOU LET ME PUT YOUR NAME FORWARD, ALL YOU WILL NEED IS SPENDING MONEY.

'COOL! BUT I'LL NEED TO ASK AT HOME FIRST!

WHAT WAS THAT ALL ABOUT THEN, BECKS? ARE YOU IN TROUBLE?

LET'S GUESS. MISS TRACY WANTED TO KNOW IF YOUR PAINTING WAS A HORSE OR A DOUBLE-DECKER BUS!

NAH! IT WAS A CAMEL!

YOU'RE WASTING YOUR TIME COS I AIN'T SAYIN'. AT LEAST NOT YET.

I WANT TO HEAR WHAT MUM AND DAD SAY BEFORE I START TO GET TOO EXCITED.

So, that night —

WHAT? YOU MEAN THE SCHOOL IS PAYING TO TAKE YOU TO PARIS?

I'LL NEED SPENDING MONEY, BUT YEAH! IF I CAN GO, THAT IS.

MMM! IT DOES SEEM A GOOD OFFER.

I THINK YOU SHOULD GO, BECKY.

REALLY? THANKS, MUM!

HUH! WHAT ABOUT ME? I'LL BE STUCK AT SCHOOL WHILE YOU'RE ENJOYING PARIS.

BET YOU WISH YOU'D STUCK IN AT ART NOW, HAYLEY!

SHE'S SO LUCKY!

And soon —

SOUNDS GREAT, BECKY. WILL YOU HAVE TIME TO DO ANY SIGHTSEEING?

OH, YEAH! IT'S NOT GOING TO BE ALL GALLERIES AND MUSEUMS.

16

17

NOT LONG NOW TILL THE TEAM ARRIVES.

NO — LOOKS LIKE HODGE AND FREDDY ARE DETERMINED TO IMPRESS THEM.

And —

WELCOME TO REDVALE, GIRLS. I HOPE YOUR STAY WILL BE A HAPPY ONE!

I'M SURE IT WILL BE. THIS PLACE LOOKS REAL COOL.

GIRLS!!!!

YEAH! *GIRLS!* ROZ TOLD US THAT IT'S MAINLY GIRLS WHO PLAY SOCCER IN AMERICAN SCHOOLS.

AND THIS LOT ARE *CHAMPIONS.*

WE SURE ARE! HOW ABOUT WE CHALLENGE YOU BOYS TO A GAME?

WELL — I . . .

GREAT IDEA. YOU'RE ON!

So —

YEAH! SIX NIL TO THE GIRLS! WHO SAYS BOYS ARE BEST AT FOOTBALL?

MY MUM SAYS GIRLS SHOULDN'T PLAY FOOTBALL. IT ISN'T LADYLIKE.

TRUST 'MY MUM SAYS' MARGARET TO THINK THAT.

IF IT WAS LEFT UP TO HER WE'D BE SITTING INSIDE WITH OUR EMBROIDERY.

OR KNITTING! BLEE!

18

THE END

19

Have fun with the Testing Time!

English

Unscramble the letters to find four 'famous' schools.

ts molse

erggna lihl

whgstora

hte mocp

I.T.

How many words of three or more letters can you make from the words below?

COMPUTER STUDIES

15 - 20 Pass

21 - 30 Merit

Over 31 Distinction

Geography

Which capital city goes with which country?

Madrid	Austria
Washington	Greece
Rome	Spain
Oslo	USA
Athens	Norway
Vienna	Italy

Science

These pictures all look the same, but one is slightly different. Can you spot the odd one out?

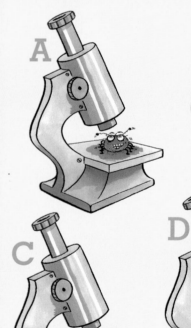

A   B

C   D

unty School Rules test!

Playtime

Just for fun - cross out any letters that appear more than once in each box to find two things we *like* at school.

O	L	O	N
N	L	R	
D	T	N	

G	I	P	A
R	M	I	E
P	S	R	I

Languages

The words below all mean 'hello' - but can you tell which language each is in?

Hola   Buongiorno

Guten Tag   Bonjour

History

Put the wives of Henry VIII in correct order.

- Catherine of Aragon
- Catherine Howard
- Anne of Cleeves
- Anne Boleyn
- Catherine Parr
- Jane Seymour

1
2
3
4
5
6

Maths

Look at the totals in the pink boxes then, using the numbers 1 to 9, fill in the yellow boxes to solve the six sums. Sums are worked from left to right and top to bottom, and each number is used only once. We've done one sum to help you start.

	+		+	11
×		+		+
8	÷	4	×	5	10
×		−		+
	÷		×		27

48	5	21

21

SCHOOL RULES!

The Four Marys

SCHOOL RULES!

THE FOUR MARYS, Cotter, Field, Radleigh and Simpson, were best friends at St Elmo's School for Girls —

GIRLS, I'D LIKE YOU TO MEET RACHEL. SHE'LL BE WITH US FROM NOW ON.

SHE LOOKS NICE. LET'S GO AND SAY 'HI'.

A few minutes later —

HI, WE'RE ALL CALLED MARY. WE CAN SHOW YOU AROUND IF YOU LIKE.

THAT'LL BE GREAT, THANKS.

HUH! WHAT A BUNCH OF GOODY-TWO-SHOES!

YEAH! SWOTS!

SHUT UP, YOU TWO.

JUST IGNORE MABEL AND VERONICA. EVERYONE ELSE DOES.

WE'LL TAKE YOU UP TO THE DORM AFTER CLASS.

Work began on the next issue. Then —

I'M WRITING A REPLY HERE TO SOMEONE WHO'S BEING BULLIED. IT'S A BIT LIKE RACHEL'S WRITING.

LET'S HAVE A LOOK, COTTY.

YEAH! SHE'S TRIED TO DISGUISE IT, BUT I'M *SURE* THIS IS RACHEL'S WRITING. SHE ALWAYS USES A DARK BLUE ROLLERBALL, DOESN'T SHE?

YEAH, I THINK YOU'RE RIGHT, SIMPY. SO WHAT DOES SHE SAY?

SHE'S BEING PICKED ON BY TWO GIRLS WHO LIE IN WAIT FOR HER EVERY DAY. SHE HATES IT HERE AND WANTS THE BULLYING TO STOP.

POOR RACHEL! WE'VE GOT TO HELP HER!

WELL, THERE ARE NO PRIZES FOR GUESSING WHO THE BULLIES ARE! MABEL AND VERONICA! THEY'RE ALWAYS PICKING ON PEOPLE AND WE'VE ALREADY SEEN THEM BEING NASTY TO RACHEL.

SIMPY'S RIGHT! AND IF THAT'S THE CASE, WE CAN EASILY DO SOMETHING ABOUT IT.

The Marys marched off to tackle Mabel and Veronica.

...AND IF YOU DON'T LEAVE RACHEL ALONE FROM NOW ON, WE'LL REPORT YOU TO MRS MITCHELL!

WHAT ARE YOU ON ABOUT?

WE'VE HARDLY EVEN *SPOKEN* TO HER!

YEAH! WHAT WOULD WE WANT WITH A SAD LITTLE WIMP LIKE HER? LEAVE US ALONE!

YEAH! THANKS TO US SHE'S GOING TO SHOP THE BULLIES. I THINK YOU OWE US AN APOLOGY — A BIG ONE!

ER, YEAH, RIGHT. SORRY, YOU TWO.

The bullies were expelled —

IMAGINE MABEL AND VERONICA HELPING TO GET RID OF THE SCHOOL BULLIES!

YEAH! WHY DIDN'T *WE* THINK OF GETTING RACHEL TO TELL MRS MITCHELL WHAT WAS GOING ON?

ACTUALLY, THAT WAS THE ADVICE I GAVE SOMEONE IN THE FIRST ISSUE OF THE MAGAZINE. I SHOULD HAVE REMEMBERED.

BUT WE CAME CHASING AFTER MABEL AND VERONICA INSTEAD!

WELL, AT LEAST RACHEL SEEMS HAPPIER — THAT'S THE MOST IMPORTANT THING.

YEAH — IT'S JUST A SHAME WE'LL HAVE TO BE NICE TO MABEL AND VERONICA FOR A WHILE!

THAT'S GOING TO BE A *REAL* PROBLEM!

LET'S WRITE INTO THE SCHOOL MAG ABOUT IT THEN!

HA, HA, HA!

THE END

SCARE

noticed the cottage door was ajar. Suddenly curious, she pushed the door open and crept in. Tiptoeing softly, she headed for the living room.

There, sitting on the floor, was Mrs Fox. She was weeping noisily and rubbing her elbow. She'd obviously fallen and hurt herself. Katy watched her wiping away her tears, and suddenly felt very sorry for her. She might be a witch, but she was hurt and needed help. Taking a deep breath, she pushed open the door and walked in.

SUDDENLY KATY FELT MUCH BRAVER ...

Are - are you all right?" she stuttered, bending close to the old lady.

Immediately, Mrs Fox stopped crying. She stared at Katy with piercing eyes. "Be a dear and help me up," she said, taking Katy's hand.

Katy grasped Mrs Fox by the arm, and heaved her to her feet. For such a thin woman, she was quite heavy.

The old woman slumped into an armchair, then blew her nose.

"I've had a bad fall," she told Katy, showing her a bruised elbow. "It's lucky you came, or I might never have got up." Sitting there with a red nose and tearful eyes, Mrs Fox didn't look much like a witch. She just looked like a frail old lady.

A full moon shone. Katy crept up the garden path towards the magic cottage where Mrs Fox lived. Her dare was to knock on the door and speak to Mrs Fox - an especially scary dare, because Mrs Fox was a witch!

Katy reached the door and hesitated. She'd felt so brave that morning when she'd agreed to the dare. But now - what if Mrs Fox cast a spell on her? What if she met that mean-looking black cat? She stared at the door for ages, trying to build up some courage. Suddenly, she heard a dreadful moaning from inside the cottage.

Katy turned cold and got ready to run, but then she

...DY-CAT!

"Can I get you anything?" Katy asked, suddenly feeling much braver.

"Yes, dear," Mrs Fox replied. "You could brew us some tea, and fetch my delicious home-made biscuits."

While Katie worked in the kitchen, searching cupboards for tea, sugar, milk and biscuits, Mrs Fox chatted to her from the living room. She asked all about Katy - her school, her favourite subjects, her hobbies and her family. Just as Katy was setting the tray onto a small table by the fire, the fearsome black cat sloped into the room. He stared at Katy with huge green eyes.

"Here's Samson," Mrs Fox said. "Samson, meet Katy, my new friend."

Immediately, Samson began rubbing against Katy's legs and purring. Katy reached down to stroke him. "He's lovely!" she exclaimed.

"Of course he's lovely. Why are you so surprised?" Mrs Fox asked.

Katy blushed. "I've been so stupid," she told Mrs Fox. "You won't believe it, but I've been afraid of you and Samson for years." Katy giggled. "I thought you both did magic."

Mrs Fox's eyes sparkled with laughter. "Not all magic is bad, Katy," she replied. "Anyway, you will visit again, won't you?"

"Of course," Katy replied. "But now I'll have to go.

THE GATE SWUNG OPEN ...

As Katy walked back down the garden path, Samson trotted beside her, jumping onto the garden fence to say goodbye.

"'Bye, Samson," Katy whispered, planting a kiss between his ears.

Samson purred loudly.

Katy went to open the gate. Suddenly, the latch clicked and the gate swung open by itself. Katy froze, staring in disbelief. Cautiously, she stepped through it, then turned back just in time to see the wooden gate close itself once more.

Amazed, Katy turned to Samson. "Samson, is there something you and Mrs Fox aren't telling me?" she asked.

Samson just winked.

31

Girl Zone

I WANT TO BE A VET

When you take your pet to the vet for treatment, do you ever wonder what it would be like to work with animals? Michaela said she'd like to find out more about a vet's job, so we went along with her.

Hi, I'm Michaela. This is Hamish, my dog. We've brought him along by car to see the vet.

Hamish has had a sore ear and the vet is going to take a look at it to see if it's okay now. We take him in on his lead.

33

Oh - oh! Looks like he read the sign! No sneaking back to the car!

When we go in, the practice manager looks up Hamish's file on the computer. There it is on the screen.

While we are waiting, the vet has other animals to look at. She asks me if I'd like to watch. Yes, please! This rabbit is in for a check-up.

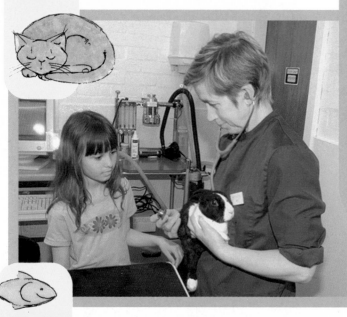

After examining him, the vet listens to his heartbeat. It's beating very fast, but that's normal! The bunny is fit and healthy so he can go home.

The surgery has a hospital attached to it where sick animals are kept in for treatment. Some of them are having operations, like Shona, the collie.

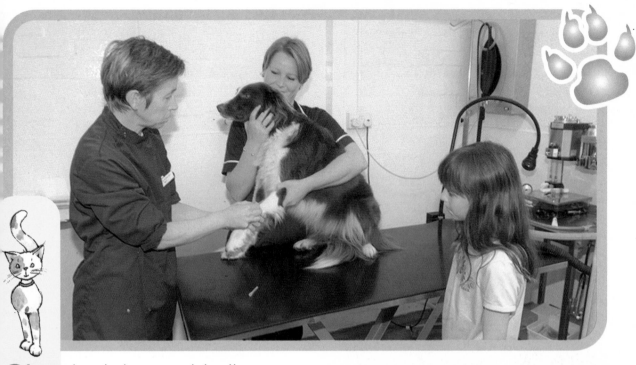

Shona has to have an injection before the operation. She sits very still.

Afterwards, Shona has to have a funny collar fitted round her neck. It looks like a big bucket! The vet explains that it will stop her licking the place where she has stitches and give it a chance to heal quickly.

Shona is put into a kennel to have a rest and then it's Hamish's turn to be examined. His ear is fine, so it's time to go home.

I had a super time seeing how the vet works with her patients. I know what I want to do when I grow up - I want to be a vet!

The Dog Next Door
ELLIE ROBINSON had a lonely life at home. She was an only child and nobody of her own age lived nearby.
FOR SALE
SORRY I CAN'T GO SWIMMING WITH YOU TODAY, ELLIE. I'VE GOT A COMMITTEE MEETING.
IT'S OKAY, MUM. I'LL JUST READ OR SOMETHING.
ANIMAL MAGIC
Then, a couple of weeks later —
REMOV
SOLD
THERE'S A NEW COUPLE MOVED IN NEXT DOOR, ELLIE.
GREAT! MAYBE THEY'LL HAVE KIDS OF ABOUT MY AGE.
Ellie's mum called round to welcome the new neighbours, but —
I'M NOT OPENING THE DOOR TO YOU! CLEAR OFF!
WELL, REALLY!

Very early next morning —

At breakfast —

And —

But next morning —

DOESN'T THAT MUTT EVER SLEEP?

I'LL GO BACK ROUND TO SORT THINGS OUT.

IT'S A GOOD EXCUSE TO SEE ANDY AGAIN.

SORRY. I KNOW SIMBA HAS BEEN NOISY AGAIN.

YOU'LL HAVE TO DO SOMETHING. MUM AND DAD ARE GOING MAD!

MAYBE I SHOULD OFFER TO SHOW ANDY AND SIMBA ROUND THE NEIGHBOURHOOD.

GOT TO GO NOW. I'LL KEEP SIMBA QUIET, I PROMISE.

Back home —

IF THAT DOG WAKES US UP AGAIN, I'M GOING TO PUT IN A COMPLAINT. DO YOU HEAR ME, ELLIE?

I COULD TAKE ANDY TO THE PARK. SIMBA WOULD LIKE THAT, TOO. THEN THERE'S THE MILL BY THE RIVER . . .

Later that day —

THAT DOG'S BARKING AGAIN! I'VE HAD ENOUGH — I'M CALLING THE POLICE.

NO, WAIT! LET ME SEE WHAT I CAN DO FIRST, MUM.

YOU'LL HAVE TO DO SOMETHING ABOUT SIMBA BEFORE YOU GET IN *REAL* TROUBLE!

I DON'T KNOW WHAT TO DO. SIMBA'S NORMALLY REALLY QUIET.

Just then —

ANDY, WHAT ARE YOU — OH, HELLO. YOU MUST BE FROM NEXT DOOR. I'VE BEEN MEANING TO CALL ROUND.

ER . . . THAT MIGHT NOT BE SUCH A GOOD IDEA, MRS CARTER.

Ellie explained about her mother's first visit —

OH, NO! WAS THAT YOUR MOTHER WHO CALLED? I THOUGHT IT WAS A SALESMAN WHO HAD BEEN PESTERING ME ALL DAY. IT MUST HAVE SEEMED *SO* RUDE!

YOU'D BETTER GO AND APOLOGISE, MUM.

YES, I'LL TAKE A PEACE OFFERING OF SOME HOME-MADE CAKE. DO YOU THINK THAT'LL WORK?

MORE THAN LIKELY! AND I COULD SHOW ANDY WHERE TO WALK SIMBA. THAT MIGHT HELP SIMBA TO SETTLE DOWN, TOO.

GOOD IDEA. I'LL JUST GET HIS LEAD.

Ellie took Andy to some of her favourite places.

THAT'S THE OLD MILL. IT'S SUPPOSED TO BE HAUNTED.

IT DOESN'T LOOK VERY SPOOKY, BUT I'LL TAKE YOUR WORD FOR IT!

39

DOGS AT WORK

We all think of dogs as our pets and friends. But some dogs work hard, too! We asked some special working dogs to tell us all about themselves.

Guide Dog

My name is Minnie, and I'm a Golden Labrador guide dog for the blind. This is me as a pup! I lived with a family for a few months before I began my real training and I got the job because I'm gentle and clever. I don't mind noisy, crowded places and travel well on buses and trains. I help my owner walk without bumping into things, and lead her when we cross the road. I'm very obedient - but if my owner asks me to do something which I know might harm her, I always refuse!

Hearing Dog

I'm called Ben and I'm a West Highland Terrier. My first owner was cruel to me, so I went to live in an animal sanctuary. But because I'm so good-natured and clever, I soon found work as a hearing dog for the deaf. I listen out for all sorts of sounds to help my mistress. I nudge her awake in the morning, I let her know when the doorbell rings and also if a child in the house cries. I even lead her to safety when the fire alarm rings. When I go out, I wear a bright yellow coat so everyone knows I do a job.

HEARING DOG FOR THE DEAF

Dog for the Disabled

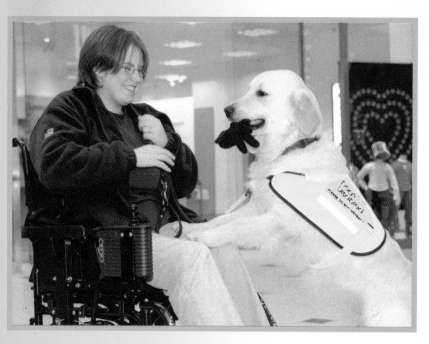

My name is Goldie and I'm a Golden Retriever. My mistress is in a wheelchair and I've been specially trained to help her because I'm so calm, friendly and clever. I fetch things for her, carry her shopping and can even take her shoes and socks off. When I'm with her, my mistress feels secure and free. When I go out, I wear a special coat so people know I'm more than just a pet.

Sheep Dog

I'm Rolo and I'm a Border Collie. My owner is a sheep farmer and I help him control his flocks. He 'talks' to me in whistles, and I herd the sheep wherever he wants them. I got this job because I'm agile, fit and alert - but especially because I'm very intelligent. In fact, I'm so clever, I need to keep busy or I get naughty. I get very impatient with people or animals who aren't as clever as me - and will nip anyone who annoys me!

Police Dog

I'm called Max and I'm a German Shepherd who works as a police dog. My mistress is a policewoman who got me when I was three months old. I had to train hard to do my job. I can chase and restrain a criminal, follow a scent and control crowds. If someone threatens my mistress with a weapon, I take it away from them! I'm really fit so I can run fast and jump or climb over loads of things. I never disobey my mistress - even when I really want to - and because I'm so strong, clever and fearless, I make a terrific police dog!

Rescue Dog

I'm called Bonnie and I'm a Newfoundland dog who lives in the countryside. Most of the time I'm a family pet but, when someone goes missing, I become a rescue dog. I can work in all kinds of weather, day or night. I can search through dense brush, timber, snow and even water! I'm very fit and can search a large area quickly. I hunt by searching for the missing person's scent on the breeze. When I find the scent, I follow it until I find the person!

Guard Dog

My name is Butch and I'm a Rottweiler guard dog. I'm a huge, strong and confident dog who's not afraid to fight an intruder. My size, bravery and loud bark make me very frightening. But I'm also very friendly, intelligent and obedient - so my owner knows I won't really hurt anyone. That way, I don't get into trouble with the police!

Sniffer Dog

I'm Trixie and, like Max, I work for the police, too - but I'm a sniffer dog! I'm a Spaniel with a good sense of smell, and am great at sniffing out bad stuff like drugs or explosives. I can search a large building really quickly, and even find bad stuff in large crowds. I love to hunt, and always get rewarded at the end! A chew, a chocolate, or a really great cuddle!

43

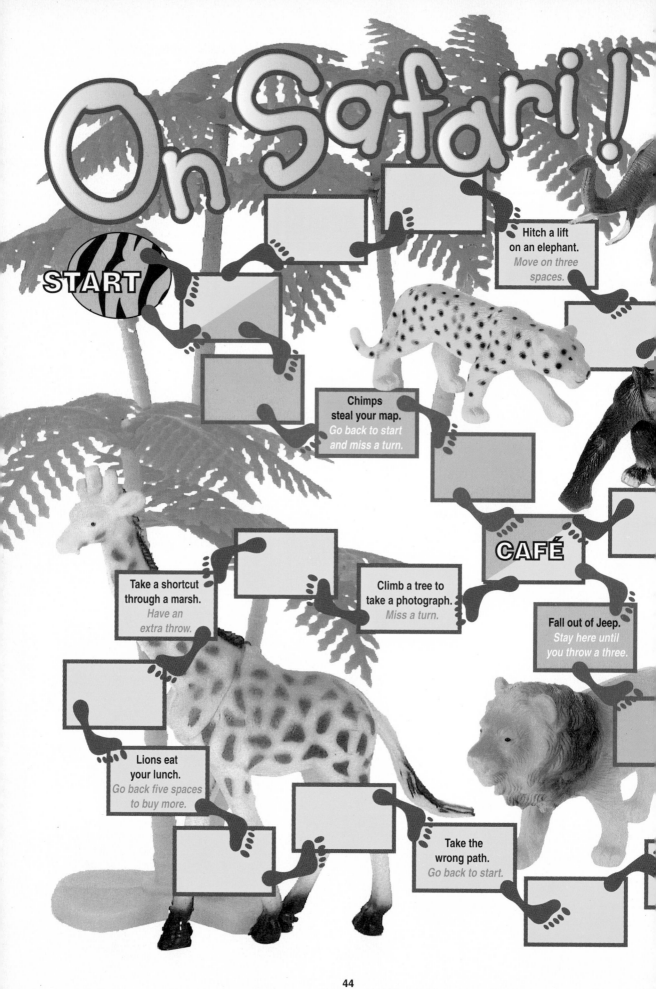

On Safari!

START

Hitch a lift
on an elephant.
*Move on three
spaces.*

Chimps
steal your map.
*Go back to start
and miss a turn.*

CAFÉ

Take a shortcut
through a marsh.
*Have an
extra throw.*

Climb a tree to
take a photograph.
Miss a turn.

Fall out of Jeep.
*Stay here until
you throw a three.*

Lions eat
your lunch.
*Go back five spaces
to buy more.*

Take the
wrong path.
Go back to start.

44

Two or more people can play this game and all you need is a marker and a dice. Decide who goes first then, *before* you throw the dice, say which path you're going to take through the 'jungle'. The yellow path is longer, but the orange path is *much* more dangerous. Any time you are sent back to the start or land on a shared square you can opt to change your path - but only *before* you throw again. You need to throw the exact amount to finish and if two or more players land on the same square at the same time, then you *all* go back to the start.

ANiMAL MAGiC

to count
a stripes.
s a turn.

Help a
wounded animal.
*Go forward
six spaces.*

Race a cheetah.
*Move forward
two spaces.*

Trip over a
hidden tree root.
*Go back one space
and miss a turn.*

Hide to
avoid a stampede.
Miss two turns.

FIRST
AID

REST
AREA

Slip and fall
into a snake pit.
*You lose
the game!!!*

e a lost
in home.
ck to start.

Hitch a lift home
in the warden's
helicopter.
You win the game!!!

FINISH

Fun with a...

... fill your room with balloons and invite your mates round for a party!

... put five pounds' worth of credit on your mobile phone and get texting!

... go for a swim! Check out the flumes, rapids and other fun things at your local leisure centre.

... start a library by buying a book or two by your fave author.

... pamper yourself with a girlie night in! Treat yourself to a face pack, conditioning hair treatment and other girlie goodies!

...go bargain hunting in sales or charity shops. You'll be amazed at what you can buy!

... pick 'n' mix a huge bag of sweets.

... treat yourself to your fave CD single, learn the words and make up your very own dance!

... buy some stamps and surprise your friends and family by sending them letters, cards, sweets and other stuff in the post!

... buy a frisbee and get out and about with your friends and pets!

HARRY POTTER and the Chamber of Secrets
J.K. ROWLING

Winner of the 1998 Smarties Gold Award

superdrug bath bubbles
GALAXY GIRL

Hello Kitty
Peach Face Pack
All skin types

Fiver!

Got a spare £5?
Check out our fab ideas on what to do with it!

... treat yourself to lots of hair accessories and have a makeover session with your mates.

... got something to say? Get it printed on a T-shirt!

... pretend you're a tourist and visit galleries and exhibitions in your town. Lots of them will be free.

...treat someone you love to something *they'd* love.

... buy five bright nail varnishes and paint them on alternate fingers and toes.

... treat yourself to a bit of jewellery. You can keep it for ever.

... get a groovy photo album and fill it with all your fave photos. Aw!

... get arty! Stock up on cheap stuff from an art shop and start making cards, calendars, collages, posters and more!

... buy a huge bag of popcorn, hire your fave video and invite round all your mates.

... buy a film for your camera and get snapping. You'll be so excited when you see your pics!

The Lost Girl

RUTH PARKER was well known around Sallowfield Market. She ran errands for the stallholders in exchange for some food.

FETCH ME A HOT PIE, RUTH — AND GET ONE FOR YOURSELF.

TA, CHARLIE. YOU'RE A GENT!

They all knew she could be trusted.

COME AND WATCH THE STALL FOR TEN MINUTES, RUTH. I KNOW YOU WON'T PINCH NOTHIN'.

I PLAY FAIR WITH HIM COS I KNOW HE'LL GIVE ME THE LEFT-OVER FRUIT AND VEG AT THE END OF THE DAY.

IT'S BEEN A GOOD DAY. I GOT A STALE LOAF, AS WELL AS THE FRUIT AND VEG.

WELL, WELL, IF IT AIN'T RUTH PARKER! REMEMBER THE RULES OF OUR GANG! SHARE AND SHARE ALIKE.

YOU MEAN YOU WANT TO PINCH EVERYTHING I EARNED TODAY, WATT DIXON.

CATCH 'ER . . . OUCH!

ONE THING I'VE LEARNED. YOU'VE GOT TO BE QUICK ON YOUR FEET AROUND HERE.

49

THAT'S HALF-A-DOZEN TIMES YOU'VE TRIPPED UP, GIRL. I SUPPOSE YOUR LEGS ARE WEAK, FROM HAVING BEEN TRUSSED UP IN THAT SACK.

HERE WE ARE! IT'S NO PALACE, BUT WHAT DO YOU THINK OF IT?

I — I DON'T KNOW. I CAN'T SEE!

WHAT DO YOU MEAN, YOU CAN'T SEE? COR — YOU'RE BLIND, AIN'T YOU?

MY HEAD HURTS — I CAN'T SEE. I-I'M LOST, RUTH. I DON'T KNOW WHO I AM!

THERE, THERE! DON'T GET INTO A STATE, ANNIE. FIRST THING TO DO IS HAVE SOMETHING TO EAT.

YOU MUST BELONG TO *SOMEONE*. UNTIL WE FIND YOUR REAL HOME, I'LL BE YOUR EYES, ANNIE. I'LL LOOK AFTER YOU.

Next morning —

WHILE I'M WORKING, I'LL LISTEN OUT FOR NEWS OF A LOST LITTLE GIRL WHO MIGHT BE YOU. MEANWHILE, TRY TO REMEMBER HOW YOU GOT IN THAT SACK!

Y-YES, RUTH.

WHAT ARE YOU DOING NOW, RUTH?

I'M HOLDING OLD SAM'S HORSE WHILE HE GOES FOR HIS DINNER. HE'LL PROBABLY GIVE US A BIT OF HIS BREAD AND CHEESE, AS WAGES.

Then —

WHAT PRIZE HAS RUTH PARKER GOT FOR HERSELF TODAY? A SKINNY BRAT TO LOOK AFTER.

WHO'S THAT, RUTH?

JUST SOMEONE WHO'S TOO BIG FOR HIS BOOTS. WAIT THERE, ANNIE. I'LL SEE 'EM OFF.

HOP IT, WATT DIXON.

RUTH . . . HELP!

SOMEONE GRABBED ME. THEY STOLE MY SHOES.

OH, NO! SORRY, ANNIE, THOSE SHOES WILL BE SOLD BEFORE WE CAN TRACK 'EM DOWN.

Several days passed —

I'VE HAD AN IDEA, ANNIE. MAYBE YOU COME FROM ONE OF THESE POSH HOUSES. WE'LL WALK ROUND THE PLACES WHERE THE RICH FOLK LIVE, AND SEE IF ANY OF IT SOUNDS FAMILIAR.

A few hours later —

I CAN'T WALK ANY FURTHER, RUTH. I STILL CAN'T REMEMBER WHERE I LIVE. I THINK YOU'LL HAVE TO BE MY EYES FOR EVER AND EVER.

LET'S GO HOME. YOU'RE WORN OUT.

52

CLEVER GIRL, ANNIE! THIS IS OUR FIRST CLUE TO FINDING OUT WHO YOU REALLY ARE. ALL WE GOT TO DO IS TRACE THAT TOFF IN THE BLACK CARRIAGE.

But another two days passed —

IT SOUNDS LIKE THERE ARE MANY CARRIAGES. CAN'T YOU SEE THE ONE WE WANT?

IT COULD TAKE WEEKS, ANNIE. WHAT WE NEED ARE MORE EYES TO HELP. I'M GOING TO PUT OUT THE WORD THAT I NEED TO SPEAK TO WATT DIXON.

And —

YOU WANT ME TO JOIN YOUR GANG BECAUSE I GET MORE PICKINGS FROM THE MARKET THAN ANY OF YOU. WELL, I AGREE — BUT YOU'VE GOT TO HELP ANNIE FIRST.

Ruth described the black carriage with the silver lamps —

I GOT MEMBERS OF MY GANG ALL OVER LONDON. I'LL PASS THE MESSAGE ROUND, AND WE'LL FIND THAT CARRIAGE BEFORE MORNING.

Sure enough, next day —

YOU DID WELL, WATT. I CAN MANAGE NOW.

WAIT A MINUTE, RUTH PARKER. IF THERE'S A REWARD FOR RETURNING THIS LOST KID, THEN IT'S FAIR SHARES, REMEMBER?

Just then —

ANNABEL — BUT YOU'RE DEAD!

UNCLE RODERICK!

YOUR MEMORY'S COME BACK!

54

THE END

55

Steppin'

1 At the school disco with your mates, what will you wear on your feet?
a) Clumpy platforms.
b) Sparkly sandals.
c) Little black pumps with bright bows.

2 You're an ugly sister in your school production of Cinderella. You can wear your own shoes, so what do you choose?
a) Big brown hiking boots - after all, you *are* an ugly sister!
b) Posh shoes. You *are* going to a ball, remember.
c) Plain flat shoes with multi-coloured tights!

3 You're pottering around at home on a wet Sunday. You're wearing...
a) ... cosy old slippers.
b) ... open-toed sandals with your toenails painted to match.
c) ... cute fluffy slippers in an animal shape.

4 The boy next door has finally asked you out. What shoes will you wear?
a) Probably your trainers. You don't want to look like you're trying *too* hard.
b) Your favourite comfy shoes so you won't worry about having sore feet.
c) Your newest shoes. You want to look your best.

5 You're on a country walk one wet weekend. You're wearing ...
a) ... sturdy sensible hiking boots. You just want to keep dry.
b) ... bright red wellies with a matching coat.
c) ... proper walking boots with multi-coloured laces.

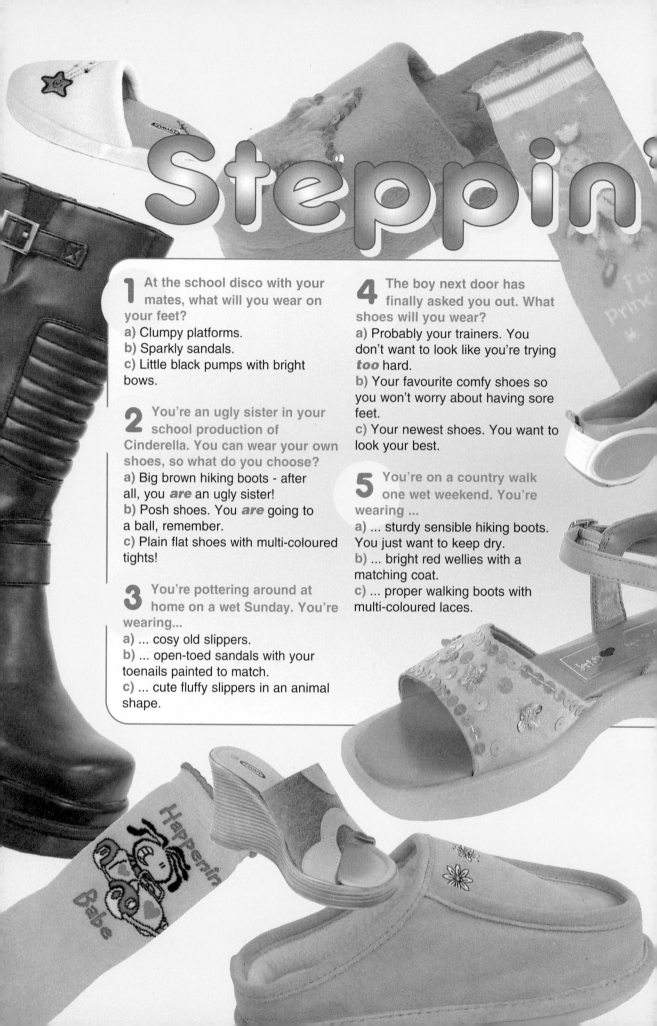

Out!

Find out what your shoes say about you with this fun quiz!

6 Your best friend is having a sleepover. What do you wear on your feet?
a) Thick comfy socks to pad about in.
b) Your latest shoes or sandals. You want to show them off.
c) Nothing! But you've painted all your toenails different colours.

7 At the beach on your summer hols, what's on your feet?
a) Fluorescent flip flops!
b) Beautiful sandals you bought in a market.
c) You're carrying your sandals and feeling the sand between your toes.

8 Shopping in town with your mates what shoes are you wearing?
a) You'll be walking for miles so you're wearing what's most comfortable.
b) Your trendiest boots. Who knows *who* you might meet?
c) Something bold and bright, like funky green trainers!

Mostly a
Miss Practical
Your friends love you because you're such good fun and don't mind getting in a mess. Now and again you like to get all dressed up and, when you do, you look stunning.

Mostly b
Miss Sophisticated
You're a supercool babe! You always look good whatever you wear. You're a natural leader - all your friends like to follow your style. Don't feel you always have to look perfect, though!

Mostly c
Miss Theatrical
You always dare to be different, so your friends think you're a good laugh. You keep coming up with new ways to have fun and cool looks for you and your friends to try.

Groovy Chick

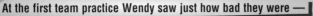

61

And by their next team practice —

I CAN'T BELIEVE THIS! YOU'RE IMPROVING, GIRLS.

IF MISS TRENCHER'S NOTICED THE DIFFERENCE, THEN WE *MUST* BE GETTING BETTER.

On the day of the game against Highcliff —

COME ON, GIRLS! WE'RE GOING TO GIVE THEM A TOUGH GAME!

But —

WAS IT 16-0 WE BEAT YOU LAST TIME?

WELL, WE'VE BEEN TRAINING HARD. THIS TIME IT WILL BE DIFFERENT!

But —

WE'RE STILL GETTING THRASHED! SO MUCH FOR MY DREAMS OF BEING ON A WINNING TEAM!

And finally —

YES! HIGHCLIFF WINS 15-2!

THE END

POPWORD

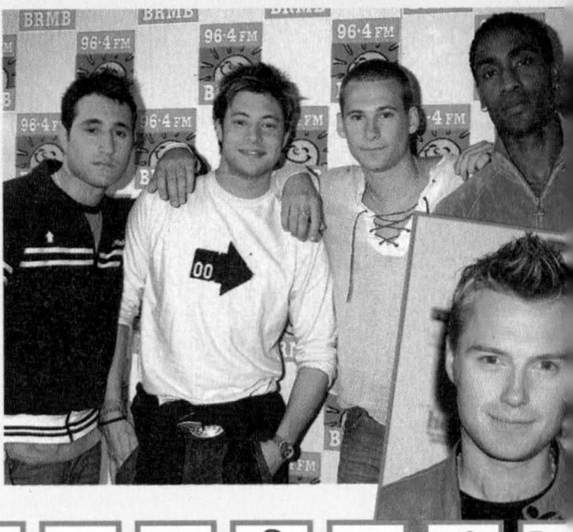

Here's a top pop crossword - just for you!

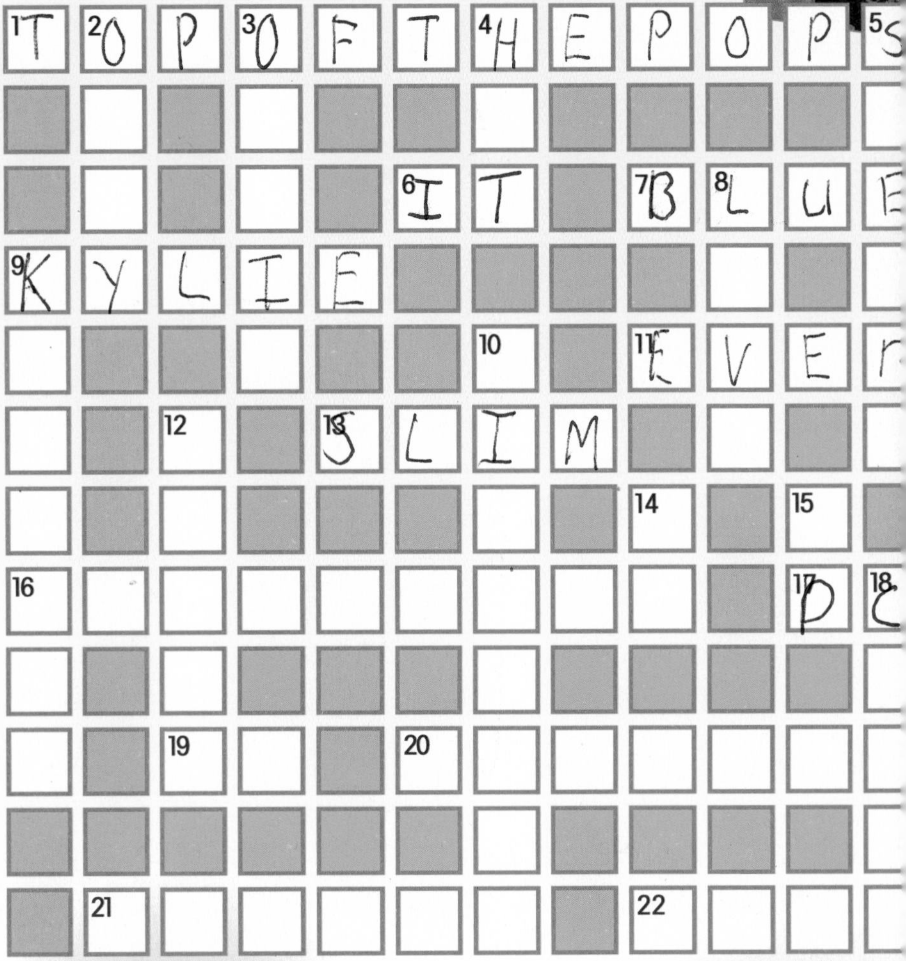

ACROSS

1. Top pop programme (3,2,3,4)
6. **'Oops I Did _ _ Again'** sang Britney (2)
7. A colourful band (4)
9. Miss Minogue (5)
11. **'When _ _ _ _, Wherever'** was a hit for Shakira (4)
13. Fat Boy _ _ _ _, Zoe Ball's husband (4)
16. Natalie _ _ _ _ _ _ _ _ _ used to act in Home And Away (9)
17. Destiny's Child initially (1,1)
19. Eminem's initials (1,1)
20. Her nickname's Madge (7)
21. Fran's the singer in this Scottish group (6)
22. **'Play'** and **'18'** were two of his albums (4)

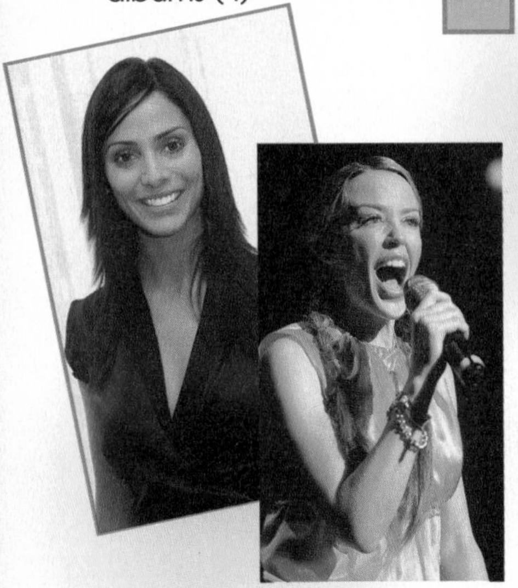

DOWN

2. **'It's _ _ _ _'** was a hit for Atomic Kitten (4)
3. Brothers Noel and Liam lead this group (5)
4. All singers want their songs to be a _ _ _ (3)
5. Britney _ _ _ _ _ _ sang **'Boys'** (6)
8. **'_ _ _ _ at First Sight'** was a hit for Kylie (5)
9. Ronan's surname (7)
10. Robbie _ _ _ _ _ _ _ _ (8)
12. A collection of singles (5)
14. Christina Aguilera's initials (1,1)
15. Compact Disc in short (1,1)
18. 'She was kind of exciting, a little _ _ _ _ _' sang Gareth Gates in **'Anyone of Us'** (5)

...SWERS
...OSS
...op of the pops, 6. It,
...lue, 9. Kylie,
...Ever, 13. Slim,
Imbruglia, 17. D.C.,
M.M (Marshall
...thers),
Madonna,
Travis, 22. Moby.
...WN
...kay, 3. Oasis, 4. Hit,
...pears, 8. Love,
...eating, 10. Williams,
Album, 14. C.A.,
C.D., 18. Crazy.

TRICK or TREAT?

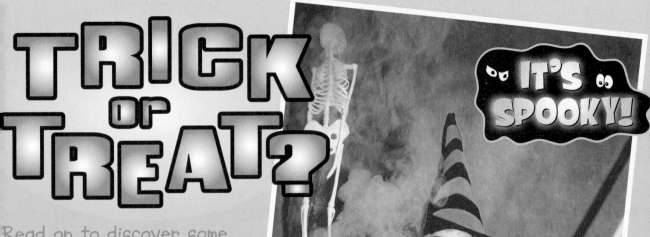

IT'S SPOOKY!

Read on to discover some spooky – and some not so spooky – Hallowe'en facts!

The name Hallowe'en comes from All Hallows' Eve. This is the night before All Hallows or All Saints' Day, which falls on November 1st.

Ancient Celts believed that Hallowe'en was the time when dead spirits came looking for bodies to possess. As no one wanted to be possessed, people dressed up in scary costumes and walked the streets making lots of noise to scare the spirits away.

Have you ever bobbed for apples? Bet you have. But did you know that the custom probably comes from an ancient Roman celebration honouring Pamona, the Roman Goddess of fruit and trees?

It was Americans who 'invented' Trick or Treat. In Scotland the custom of going round houses on Hallowe'en is called guising (from disguising). Unlike the American version, the guiser usually has to earn her reward by singing a song, telling a joke or reciting a poem.

Carrying a lantern is traditional on Hallowe'en and is thought to come from the old Irish story of Jack–o–lantern. According to the tale, poor Jack had to wander for ever with only an ember inside a hollowed–out turnip to light his way.

More people dress up as witches than anything else at Hallowe'en. Other favourite costumes are ghosts, monsters and vampires.

Pumpkins were first used as lanterns because they were more plentiful than turnips in America. They're also easier to 'hollow out'.

Hallowe'en may be spooky, but it's really much more to do with ancient customs than evil spirits, so DO NOT BE AFRAID!!!!!!

Hagatha the Witch costume from **Rubie's Masquerade.** Contact 08700 129090 for details. *(Always ask permission before using the phone.)*

Boy From Beyond

It's SPOOKY!

DO you like parties? Tanya and Fay Carter, whose father had just taken over a country hotel, were looking forward to the Hallowe'en party there —

ARE YOU NEARLY READY, TANYA?

IN A MINUTE, FAY. I JUST WANT TO SEE IF 'DARKEST NIGHT' ARE ON THIS TV SHOW.

But —

... SO ONCE AGAIN 'DARKEST NIGHT' — THE MOST ELUSIVE BAND IN THE COUNTRY — CAN'T BE WITH US.

HUH! THEY HARDLY APPEAR *ANYWHERE* THESE DAYS!

THEY'RE MY FAVOURITE BAND. LOOK! I GOT THIS PICTURE FREE WITH MY MAGAZINE.

COOL, TANYA.

NEVER MIND. DAD'S BOOKED A BAND FOR THIS PARTY TONIGHT. LET'S GO AND SEE WHAT *THEY'RE* LIKE.

ERK! CALL THAT A BAND?

THEY'VE OBVIOUSLY BEEN BOOKED TO FIT IN WITH THE OLD-FASHIONED THEME.

THE GUESTS ARE OLD-FASHIONED, TOO. AND *ANCIENT!*

I'M NOT!

I'M LUKE, FROM THE VILLAGE. I CAME HERE WITH MY PARENTS BUT — APART FROM MEETING YOU TWO — I AGREE IT LOOKS LIKE BEING A BORING NIGHT.

WHOO-OOOH!

EEK! A GHOST!

TCH! GROWN-UPS ARE WORSE THAN KIDS, SOMETIMES!

I WISH IT WERE A *REAL* GHOST. THAT WOULD LIVEN THINGS UP A BIT!

WHY DON'T WE GO FOR A WALK ROUND? THE ORIGINAL HOUSE IS VERY OLD. THERE MIGHT *BE* GHOSTS ABOUT TONIGHT.

OKAY, LUKE. COME ON, TANYA.

I DIDN'T NOTICE INSIDE, BUT LUKE'S GOT A BIT OF A LIMP.

AAAH!

FAY, WHAT'S WRONG? OH . . . !

IT'S JUST A STATUE!

IT FRIGHTENED US, THOUGH. WE HAVEN'T BEEN TO THIS PART OF THE HOTEL GROUNDS BEFORE, AND IT LOOKED DEAD SPOOKY!

EVERYTHING LOOKS SPOOKY TO ME!

Then —

LOOK! THERE ARE LIGHTS ON IN THAT OLD FARMHOUSE!

THAT'S STRANGE. IT'S DEFINITELY SUPPOSED TO BE EMPTY. DAD WAS THINKING OF BUYING IT.

I'M SORRY, I'LL HAVE TO GET OUT. I CAN'T STAND THIS NOISE!

I'LL GO WITH LUKE. BUT YOU CAN STAY, IF YOU WANT, TANYA.

OKAY.

OF *COURSE* I WANT TO STAY. THEY'RE THE MOST SECRETIVE BAND IN THE BUSINESS, YET HERE THEY ARE, JUST OVER THE ROAD FROM WHERE I LIVE!

In a break between songs —

I CAN STILL HARDLY BELIEVE IT! I MEAN, I KNOW YOU LIKE TO KEEP OUT OF THE PUBLIC EYE, BUT WHY DID YOU PICK THIS PLACE?

OUR NEXT ALBUM IS TO BE CALLED 'BOY FROM BEYOND'. IT'S ABOUT A CRIPPLED BOY WHO LIVED IN THE VILLAGE NEAR HERE CENTURIES AGO AND IS SAID TO HAUNT THE AREA.

WH-WHAT DID YOU SAY?

YOU MEAN — HE'S A GHOST?

COME ON, PETE, TIME FOR OUR NEXT SONG.

71

But inside —
WHAT? HOW?
There was no heat in the flames as the band vanished.
When Luke and Fay arrived —
WHERE HAS THE BAND GONE? I DIDN'T SEE THEM LEAVE.
YOU LOOK AS THOUGH YOU'VE SEEN A GHOST!
I — I THINK I HAVE.
BUT NO-ONE'S *EVER* GOING TO BELIEVE ME.
So, you see, there wasn't just *one* boy from beyond — there were four of them. Every member of 'Darkest Night' was a ghost and, as the singer said, ghosts visit then leave — sometimes right before your eyes.
THE END

WOOORDSEARCH!

IT'S SPOOKY!

Hidden in this word square are lots of words associated with Hallowe'en. See if you can find all of them from the list below. They can read forwards, backwards, up, down and diagonally, and each letter may be used more than once. When you have found all the words, the remaining letters will **spell** out a secret message! Have fun!

BAT
BLACK CAT
BROOMSTICK
CAULDRON
CLOAK
COBWEBS
FANCY DRESS
FLYING
FULL MOON
GHOST

HALLOWEEN
LANTERN
MAGIC
MIDNIGHT
OCTOBER
PUMPKIN
SCREAM
SPELLS
SPIDER
SPOOKY

STARS
TOAD
TRICK OR TREAT
VAMPIRE
WITCH
WIZARD

Hidden message -

WITCH IN THE SKY.
WHEN YOU MIGHT SEE A
HALLOWEEN IS THE NIGHT

B	H	A	S	S	E	R	D	Y	C	N	A	F	L
L	L	Y	K	O	O	P	S	O	W	E	N	R	E
S	N	A	N	I	V	A	M	P	I	R	E	E	S
T	R	I	C	K	O	R	T	R	E	A	T	D	W
H	E	A	K	K	C	T	H	T	G	L	E	I	I
G	B	A	T	P	C	I	N	N	O	H	L	P	T
I	O	I	C	S	M	A	T	G	C	A	O	S	C
N	T	H	O	A	L	U	T	S	T	L	D	S	H
D	C	D	B	W	U	F	P	H	M	L	O	M	T
I	O	R	W	F	U	L	L	M	O	O	N	A	E
M	N	A	E	Y	O	Y	D	U	M	W	O	E	K
I	G	Z	B	H	T	I	S	R	E	E	E	R	A
W	I	I	S	T	C	N	H	I	O	E	N	C	B
T	H	W	E	C	I	G	A	M	S	N	K	S	Y

74

It was Saturday afternoon and Jane Foreman was busy with her homework —

THAT'S ME AWAY FOR A GAME OF GOLF WITH JIM. I'LL BE BACK AROUND FIVE O'CLOCK.

OKAY, LOVE! 'BYE!

SECRETS

I'M JUST NIPPING OUT TO THE CORNER SHOP FOR SOME BUTTER, JANE.

OKAY, MUM. I'LL GET ON WITH MY ESSAY.

THERE ARE THREE PEOPLE IN MY FAMILY AND WE'RE VERY HAPPY . . . AND HUNGRY! I'LL WORK BETTER WITH A SNACK.

OH! THERE'S PLENTY OF BUTTER HERE! I'LL CALL MUM BACK.

OH, MUM'S *NOT* GOING TO THE CORNER SHOP! WHAT'S SHE DOING GOING DOWN *THERE?* A NEW MAN'S JUST MOVED INTO THAT HOUSE.

WHY DIDN'T MUM *SAY* SHE WAS GOING SOMEWHERE ELSE?

Next day —

I'LL BE BACK SOON, JANE. I'M JUST GOING TO SEE MRS GRAHAM.

OKAY, MUM. 'BYE!

BUT MRS GRAHAM ALWAYS VISITS HER SISTER ON SUNDAYS. I'M GOING TO FOLLOW MUM.

And —

AMANDA! I'M BEGINNING TO FEEL I'VE KNOWN YOU FOR YEARS.

HELLO, MARK. I'M RUNNING OUT OF EXCUSES TO GET AWAY. I HOPE ROBERT AND JANE DON'T SUSPECT ANYTHING.

OH! MUM'S DELIBERATELY TELLING LIES TO ME AND DAD! WHAT'S GOING ON?

On Monday —

MRS JONES, CAN YOU TELL ME WHO'S MOVED INTO THE COTTAGE NEAR MY HOUSE?

A MAN CALLED MR LOMAX, JANE. HE'S SO HANDSOME AND CHARMING, ISN'T HE? HE'S DIVORCED, TOO.

SURELY HE CAN'T HAVE CHARMED MY MUM? CAN HE?

On Wednesday, at school —

HAVE YOU SEE THAT MR LOMAX FROM LONDON? MY MUM THINKS HE'S GORGEOUS!

MINE, TOO! SHE RECKONS HE'LL BE CHATTING UP ALL THE WOMEN IN THE VILLAGE!

Then —

POOR FIONA! HER MUM RAN OFF WITH A DIVORCED MAN, LEAVING FIONA AND HER BROTHER WITH THEIR DAD!

OH! THAT COULDN'T HAPPEN TO ME, COULD IT?

Later, at home —

YOU AND MUM NEVER SEEM TO GO OUT ANYWHERE TOGETHER ANY MORE, DAD.

THAT OFTEN HAPPENS WHEN YOU'RE MARRIED, LOVE. PEOPLE HAVE DIFFERENT INTERESTS — LIKE I HAVE MY GOLF AND MUM HAS HER CHOIR. BUT WE STILL LOVE EACH OTHER.

OH, POOR DAD! HE DOESN'T SUSPECT A THING — AND I CAN'T TELL HIM! I WONDER IF MUM REALLY *IS* AT HER CHOIR REHEARSAL TONIGHT.

On Thursday —

IT'S DAD'S BIRTHDAY ON SATURDAY. I WANT AN EXTRA-SPECIAL CARD FOR HIM.

...SO IT LOOKS LIKE MR LOMAX HAS A NEW GIRLFRIEND.

OH, NO! MUM *MUST* BE SEEING MR LOMAX! POOR DAD!

On Saturday —

DAD'S GOING OUT FOR A GAME OF GOLF SOON, BUT MUM HASN'T SAID A WORD ABOUT HIS PRESENT. IT'S USUALLY WRAPPED UP AND WAITING FOR HIM AT BREAKFAST. OH, DEAR!

Then —

OH! IT'S MR LOMAX! HE'S COME *HERE*!

JANE! WILL YOU COME DOWNSTAIRS, PLEASE?

MR LOMAX IS HERE TO TAKE MUM AWAY — AND ON DAD'S BIRTHDAY, TOO!

LOOK — MR LOMAX IS AN ARTIST AND HE'S DONE THIS WONDERFUL PAINTING OF YOUR MUM FOR MY BIRTHDAY. ISN'T IT LOVELY?

I WANTED IT TO BE A SURPRISE FOR YOU BOTH, BUT IT'S BEEN *SO* DIFFICULT KEEPING MY SITTINGS WITH MARK A SECRET.

OOPS! LOOKS LIKE ALL MY WORRYING WAS FOR NOTHING. I'VE ACTUALLY GOT A *MODEL* MUM! THANK GOODNESS!

THE END

Want to know your lucky number? Just write down your date of birth and keep adding all the numbers together until you get one number.

What's Your Number?

Here's an example:
Date of birth: 11.4.94   1+1+ 4+9+4 =19   1+9 =10   1+0 =1

Now check out your lucky number to see what it says about you!

1
You are a happy soul who is ruled by the sun. You're great at coming up with new ideas and you love meeting new people. You have lots of friends and your hobbies include dancing, drama and sunbathing. You're also good at sports but you can be a little impatient.

You love: Parties, gold jewellery, make-up.
You hate: Waiting, having no money, spending time on your own.

2
You're ruled by the moon and are sometimes sensitive and shy. You like looking after animals and meeting up for a natter with your mates. You hate surprises and don't like sudden changes in routine. Friends always know you will keep your promises.

You love: Peace and quiet, pets, swimming.
You hate: Meeting new people, fireworks, loud music.

3
Jupiter is your ruling planet, making you quite an impulsive person. You're excellent at solving problems and usually look on the bright side of life. You enjoy helping people and are very popular. You're always in demand for fundraising events.

You love: Books, all kinds of music, sports.
You hate: Being cold, grumpy friends, wasting time.

4 Your ruling planet is Saturn, which means you're a hard worker. You're always ready to help out at home, especially in the garden. You hate being cooped up indoors when you could be out for a walk with a pet or a mate. Friends think you're a good laugh.

You love: Plants, reading, sunbathing.
You hate: Rain, people who don't laugh at your jokes, bullies.

Magazine

5 Mercury, the planet of communication, is your ruling planet, so you're happiest texting, phoning and chatting to your mates. You're always on the go and rarely take time to relax, unless it's to have a long texting session with a friend!

You love: Talking, quizzes, computers.
You hate: Silence, cooking, waiting in queues.

P.C. ?

6 You're very girlie, being ruled by Venus, and love buying clothes, make up and shoes. If you see sparkly stuff, you've just got to buy it. You sometimes run out of money, despite being a brill bargain hunter. Your friends often ask your advice on what to buy.

You love: Fashion, perfume, shopping.
You hate: Untidiness, windy days, being copied.

fashion

Uranus, your ruling planet, is the planet of change, so your life is usually full of excitement and suspense. You're keen to try new things and visit places you've never seen before. You get impatient with people who don't share your sense of adventure.

You love: Theme parks, mystery tours, surprises.
You hate: Being told what to do, timetables, having to be punctual.

7

surprise

1st

8

Mars is your ruling planet, so you tend to be full of energy and enthusiasm. You like playing and watching sports and you hate losing! Your competitive nature sometimes annoys your friends, but you're still a very good, reliable mate.

You love: Watching sport on TV, winning at everything you do, chocolate.
You hate: Sitting still, forgetful friends, being late.

9

You're very imaginative, having Neptune as your ruling planet. This means you like being out in the country, drawing and making things. Presents for your friends are always beautifully wrapped and take you ages to choose.

You love: Painting, picnics, movies.
You hate: Long car journeys, being stuck inside on sunny days, maths.

Movies

ADD 'EM UP!

What number do you get if you add up the numbers on which the following days land?
e.g. Hallowe'en = (Oct) 31

Valentine's Day

+

Guy Fawkes' Day

+

Christmas Day

+

New Year's Day

= 45

WORK

Two pages of puzzles — just for you

IN A SWIRL!

Write the answers to these clues in the swirl and you'll find that the last letter of each answer is the first letter of the next answer.

1. This grows into an oak tree (5)
2. The opposite of day (5)
3. A shape with three sides (8)
4. You see with these (4)
5. Making no noise (6)
6. Baby frogs (8)
7. Ice cream pudding with nuts, cream and sauce (6)

IT-OUT!

AMAZING!

Which path will lead you to the centre of our maze - A, B, C or D?

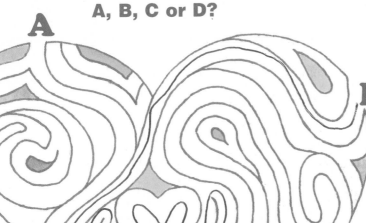

A
B
C
D

NINE 2 FIVE!

Turn **NINE** to **FIVE** in two steps, changing just one letter at a time.

NINE

F I N E

FIVE

MAGIC!

Slot these two sets of words into their grids in the correct order, and they'll read the same across as they do down.

1. ENDS, FIVE, IRON, VOID
2. NINE, OMIT, SONS, STEM

1

F	I	V	E
I	R	O	N
V	O	I	D
E	N	D	S

2

S	O	N	S
O	M	I	T
N	I	N	E
S	T	E	M

IN COLOUR!

Can you write a word in the gap which will go with the words before and after it? It's easy!

1. NAVY (_BLUE_) BELL
2. GOLD (_ _ _ _) BIN
3. ORANGE (_ _ _ _) OFF
4. BROWN (_ _ _ _ _ _) STICK
5. GREEN (_ _ _ _ _ _) WORK
6. BLACK (_ _ _) CREAM
7. GREY (_ _ _ _ _) DOG
8. WHITE (_ _ _ _ _ _) CUP
9. RED (_ _ _ _ _) PETAL
10. SILVER (_ _ _ _ _ _) WINNER

It happened to me...

MUM and Dad had always been quite well off, so I suppose I had been spoiled since I was a baby. I got my first bike before any of my friends, never had to miss a school trip, and each birthday I got exactly what I wanted. Besides, I knew how to twist Mum and Dad round my little finger. If they ever looked like refusing me anything, all I had to do was turn on the tears. I *always* got my own way after that!

✶ ✶ ✶

When they announced that Dad was leaving his job to start up his own business, I didn't pay much attention. They'd talked about this for years, but nothing ever happened, so I wasn't all that interested. But then Mum mentioned moving house!

"Moving house!" I gasped! "Why? And to where?"

"Haven't you been listening to a word we were saying?" Mum sighed. "We need to sell this house to raise money for the business. We'll be moving to a smaller place - not too far away, hopefully, so you shouldn't have to change schools."

"What?" I could hardly speak. Then I started to laugh. Mum loved our house, so there was no *way* she'd leave. But I was wrong.

"We're serious, Rosie," Mum said quietly. "All our savings are going into starting the business, so we will need to watch the pennies very carefully for the first year or so. But it's really exciting, isn't it?"

"Exciting?" I felt a bit sick. "I think it's gross! And - and when's this all going to happen?"

"Right now!" said Dad. "We're seeing the estate agent tomorrow."

"You're going to have a busy holiday this year, Rosie," Mum attempted to sound cheerful. "What with all the packing and everything!"

"So we're still going to the villa, then?" I brightened at the thought of our summer house in Majorca. "Isn't *it* getting sold too?"

"No," said Mum, "but *we* won't be going. We're renting it out this summer to raise money."

That was the final straw. Moving house was bad enough, but no holiday was unbearable. It was time to turn on the tears.

"You - you don't love me, do you?" I stammered between sobs. "If you did, you wouldn't do this! You're breaking my heart - but you don't care!" I was going way over the top, but I wanted to make sure I got my own way on this.

But Mum and Dad stayed

silent and, when I turned to look at them, I realised that they looked almost angry.

"That was the most selfish, self-centred display I've ever seen," Mum said quietly. "Even from *you*, Rosie. I know we've spoilt you in the past, and given in when we maybe should have been a bit firmer, but that was because we loved you so much."

"And you know that we've talked about starting our own business for years," Dad continued. "We've always been happy for you to have what you want, so can't you please be happy for us now?"

✶ ✶ ✶

As I dried my eyes, Mum came over and put an arm round me.

"I know it'll be hard, but it'll only be for a couple of years, until the business gets on its feet," she said. "After that, we might be even *better* off than we are now! Think about *that*."

I managed a weak smile. For the first time in my life I hadn't got what I wanted - even with tears - but it didn't feel as bad as I'd thought it might.

"I'll hold you to that," I grinned. "And I'm sorry I was so selfish, Dad. I really *am* happy for you - *honestly* !" And you know what? I really meant it!

86

A Friend in Need

After school —

SEE YOU IN THE MORNING, JEN.

I WISH I DIDN'T LIVE AT THE OPPOSITE END OF TOWN FROM MY MATES. IT MEANS I DON'T GET THE CHANCE TO SEE THEM AFTER SCHOOL.

DELLA PEARSON'S THE ONLY GIRL WHO LIVES ANYWHERE NEAR ME. HER MUM PICKS HER UP, THANK GOODNESS. IT WOULDN'T BE MUCH FUN GETTING STUCK NEXT TO HER ON THE BUS.

Then, a few days later —

WHAT AN IDIOT I AM! I'VE LEFT MY BAG SOMEWHERE AROUND THE SCHOOL, BUT I CAN'T REMEMBER WHERE.

MAYBE SOMEBODY HANDED IT IN TO LOST PROPERTY.

Mrs Quick was in charge of lost property.

STAFF ROOM

YOUR BAG ISN'T HERE. I HOPE YOU REALISE THAT YOUR PARENTS WILL BE RESPONSIBLE FOR REPLACING LOST BOOKS.

OH — I'M SURE IT'LL TURN UP.

Back in class —

HOW ON EARTH WILL I DO MY HOMEWORK WITHOUT A TEXT BOOK?

NO PROBLEM! GET YOUR DAD TO DRIVE YOU OVER TO MY PLACE TONIGHT, AND WE'LL SHARE MINE.

Dad agreed, but —

THIS IS A REAL NUISANCE, JENNY. YOU KNOW I'M BUSY IN THE EVENINGS.

I CAN'T TELL DAD MY BOOKS ARE LOST. HE'LL GO MAD IF HE THINKS HE'S GOT TO FORK OUT FOR NEW ONES. BUT WHAT WILL I DO IF THEY DON'T TURN UP?

88

Next morning —

LOOK! SOMEONE MUST HAVE FOUND MY BAG AND HUNG IT ON MY PEG.

OH, NO! EVERYTHING'S HERE EXCEPT MY TEXT BOOKS.

YOU'D BETTER REPORT THEM STOLEN TO MRS QUICK.

NO WAY! SHE'LL SEND MY DAD THE BILL. BUT I CAN'T KEEP COMING OVER TO YOUR HOUSE. IT'S TOO FAR. WHAT'LL I DO?

YOU CAN ALWAYS COME TO *MY* HOUSE TO DO YOUR HOMEWORK. I LIVE QUITE NEAR.

OH — ER — THANKS, DELLA. I'M SURE I'LL MANAGE SOMEHOW. THERE ARE PROBABLY SPARE COPIES OF THE BOOKS IN THE SCHOOL LIBRARY.

IMAGINE — DELLA PEARSON INVITING YOU ROUND!

WHAT A MEGA-BORE *THAT* WOULD BE!

But later —

THERE'S NOT A SINGLE COPY OF THE BOOKS I NEED. THERE'S ONLY ONE THING I CAN DO!

ER — IS YOUR OFFER STILL OPEN, ABOUT COMING ROUND TO YOUR PLACE THIS EVENING, DELLA?

OF COURSE.

So, that evening, at Della's house —

YOU USE THE FRENCH BOOK WHILE I DO THE MATHS HOMEWORK. THEN WE'LL SWOP OVER.

And when they were finished —

IT WAS A NICE CHANGE, DOING HOMEWORK WITH SOMEONE ELSE.

BUT YOU ENJOY WORKING, DON'T YOU? YOU MUST SPEND HOURS EVERY EVENING, TO GET THE MARKS YOU DO.

THE ONLY REASON I WORK SO HARD IS THAT IT HELPS TO PASS THE TIME. I DON'T REALLY KNOW MANY PEOPLE, SO I'VE NOTHING MUCH ELSE TO DO.

UNTIL YOUR OWN BOOKS TURN UP, YOU'RE VERY WELCOME TO WORK HERE EVERY EVENING.

I DAREN'T ASK DAD FOR NEW BOOKS SO DELLA'S OFFER IS THE ONLY ANSWER.

Then, one morning —

DELLA — WHAT ARE YOU DOING ON THE BUS? YOU ALWAYS COME TO SCHOOL BY CAR.

MUM'S NEVER FANCIED ME TRAVELLING ALONE, BUT WHEN I SAID I COULD MEET UP WITH YOU, SHE DIDN'T MIND.

PAY HERE

IT'S OKAY, ISN'T IT? YOU DON'T MIND.

ER — NO, OF COURSE NOT.

90

By the following week —

SEE YOU TONIGHT THEN? WE CAN WATCH 'TOP OF THE POPS' AFTER, IF WE WORK QUICKLY.

SHE'S GETTING TO BE QUITE HUMAN NOW SHE'S COMING OUT OF HER SHELL. MAYBE SHE'S JUST VERY SHY.

But when Jenny's friends found out —

WATCH IT, JEN! GETTING FRIENDLY WITH SWOTTY DELLA PEARSON COULD DAMAGE YOUR IMAGE. YOU COULD END UP AS TEACHER'S PET!

OH, WE'RE NOT THAT FRIENDLY, HONESTLY.

DELLA'S SAVED ME A PLACE AT HER TABLE BUT I'LL PRETEND I'VE NOT NOTICED HER. I DON'T WANT TO RISK UPSETTING KATH AND SUE BY BEING TOO MATEY WITH DELLA.

That evening —

I WON TWO FREE TICKETS TO THE CINEMA. WOULD YOU COME ON SATURDAY?

I LIKE TO KEEP SATURDAY FREE IN CASE THERE'S A CHANCE OF SEEING KATH OR SUE. I'LL HAVE TO PUT HER OFF.

OH, WE'VE GOT RELATIVES COMING THIS WEEKEND. I'D BETTER STAY AT HOME.

HISTORY

YOU DON'T HAVE TO MAKE EXCUSES JUST BECAUSE YOU DON'T WANT TO COME.

NOW I'VE UPSET HER. SHE MIGHT NOT ASK ME ROUND THEN I'D HAVE TO ASK DAD FOR THOSE NEW BOOKS.

ON SECOND THOUGHTS, THEY'LL ALL HAVE SO MUCH TO TALK ABOUT, THEY WON'T MISS ME. I'LL COME.

THAT'S GREAT. SEE YOU ABOUT TWO, THEN?

But, just after lunch on Saturday —

DAD'S OFFERED TO TAKE US TO THE ICE RINK, SO WE THOUGHT YOU'D LIKE TO COME.

OH, NO — I PROMISED MUM I'D TIDY MY ROOM. SORRY.

I EVEN HAD TO LIE TO MY BEST FRIENDS. THEY WOULDN'T HAVE UNDERSTOOD WHY I HAD TO MEET DELLA. I'D MUCH RATHER BE SKATING.

TODAY
NIGHT TERROR III

But surprisingly —

THIS IS A BRILL FILM. I DIDN'T REALISE YOU LIKED HORROR MOVIES.

I LOVE 'EM! WE'LL HAVE TO COME AGAIN.

COMING IN FOR COFFEE?

THANKS.

I'M ALMOST GLAD SOMEONE TOOK MY BOOKS. IF THEY HADN'T, I'D NEVER HAVE DISCOVERED THAT DELLA CAN BE REALLY GOOD COMPANY WHEN YOU GET TO KNOW HER.

OH, DELLA, WHEN I WAS CLEANING YOUR ROOM I FOUND THESE BOOKS HAD FALLEN DOWN BEHIND YOUR WARDROBE. THEY'VE GOT JENNY'S NAME ON THEM.

I DON'T BELIEVE IT! MY MISSING BOOKS!

YOU WERE THE THIEF!

I DIDN'T SET OUT TO STEAL THEM. I FOUND YOUR BAG, BUT THEN I OVERHEARD YOU TELLING THE OTHERS THAT YOU'D NEED TO SHARE BOOKS IF YOUR OWN DIDN'T TURN UP.

I THOUGHT THAT IF YOU HAD TO SHARE MINE FOR A FEW WEEKS, YOU MIGHT GET TO KNOW ME A BIT AND WE COULD BE FRIENDS. SO I TOOK THE BOOKS OUT OF YOUR BAG — BUT I WAS GOING TO GIVE THEM BACK.

YOU KNEW I WAS DREADING MY DAD GETTING A BILL FOR THOSE LOST BOOKS, BUT YOU LET ME GO ON WORRYING! A FUNNY KIND OF FRIEND YOU TURNED OUT TO BE.

On Monday, Jenny admitted everything to Sue and Kath.

CHEER UP, YOU'VE GOT YOUR BOOKS BACK AND YOU NEEDN'T BOTHER WITH GHASTLY DELLA AGAIN.

BUT THAT'S THE TROUBLE — SHE'S NOT THAT GHASTLY WHEN YOU GET TO KNOW HER.

IT MUST BE AWFUL TO BE SO LONELY THAT YOU'D PULL A TRICK LIKE THAT. MAYBE I WAS A BIT HARD ON HER. I'M GOING TO APOLOGISE.

YOU DON'T HAVE TO BE SORRY FOR ME. I THINK I REALLY KNEW ALL THE TIME THAT YOU WERE ONLY PUTTING ON AN ACT BECAUSE I WAS USEFUL TO YOU.

I'LL FIND A TRUE FRIEND ONE DAY, BUT IT'LL BE SOMEONE WHO REALLY WANTS TO BE MY FRIEND — NOT LIKE YOU, JENNY PARKER!

I ASKED FOR THAT. IT'S A PITY, BECAUSE I ENDED UP REALLY LIKING DELLA — BUT IT'S TOO LATE NOW.

THE END

ARE YOU A MAGIC MATE?

TRY OUR FUNKY FLOWCHART TO FIND OUT!

START ▶

YOU GET AN INVITE TO A REALLY COOL PARTY. DO YOU ASK IF YOU CAN BRING YOUR BEST MATE? — **Y** / **N**

DO YOU ALWAYS WANT TO BE THE CENTRE OF ATTENTION? — **Y** / **N**

DO YOU FIND IT HARD TO KEEP SECRETS? — **Y** / **N**

DO YOU ALWAYS RETURN THINGS AFTER FRIENDS LEND THEM TO YOU? — **Y**

DO YOU SPEAK TO YOUR BEST BUDDY EVERY DAY? — **N** / **Y**

DO YOU SPEND AS MUCH TIME AS POSSIBLE WITH ONE FRIEND? — **Y** / **N**

DO YOU SOMETIMES BUY YOUR PAL LITTLE PRESSIES FOR NO REASON? — **Y**

DO YOU HELP FRIENDS WITH HOMEWORK? — **N** / **Y**

A FRIEND DOES SOMETHING SILLY AND BEGS YOU TO KEEP QUIET. DO YOU TELL? — **N**

YOUR MATE BORROWS YOUR FAVE TOP AND RIP IT. DO YOU HAVE A MAJOR ROW — **N** / **Y**

DO YOU ALWAYS KNOW WHEN YOUR BEST FRIEND IS UPSET OR WORRIED? — **N** / **Y**

WOULD YOU LIE TO STOP A PAL GETTING INTO TROUBLE? — **Y** / **N**

WOULD YOU FEEL SECRETLY PLEASED IF YOUR CLOSEST MATE GOT INTO TROUBLE? — **N** / **Y**

DO FRIENDS OFTEN COME TO YOU FOR ADVICE? — **Y** / **N**

WOULD YOU FORGIVE A FRIEND IF SHE TOLD ONE OF YOUR SECRETS? — **N** / **Y**

DO YOU ALWAYS STAND UP FOR YOUR PAL? — **Y** / **N**

HAVE YOU EVER FORGOTTEN YOUR BEST FRIEND'S BIRTHDAY? — **N** / **Y**

MAGIC MATE
You're a forever friend! You're caring, loyal and work hard at being a great mate. Every girl should have a pal like you!

FAIR FRIEND
You're a good friend, but can be a bit gossipy and sometimes even a teensy bit jealous! With just a little more effort, you'd soon make a Magic Mate!

PERHAPS PAL
You need to try a bit harder at being a good friend. Perhaps if you spent more time together you could work towards being Magic Mates too!

Polly Banks, an orphan, was happy living at West Park Home. One afternoon in summer —

HERE, POLLY — PUT SOME CREAM ON IF YOU'RE GOING TO SIT OUT IN THE SUN.

OKAY, MRS LOWDEN. THANKS.

A Dream Come True

MRS LOWDEN'S REALLY NICE TO US ALL — BUT I WISH I HAD A REAL MUM AND DAD AGAIN. I MISS NOT BEING PART OF A FAMILY.

Later —

OH, THERE'S KAREN COMING BACK FROM VISITING THE NICOLLS AGAIN. THEY SEEM TO REALLY LIKE HER. LUCKY THING!

When Polly met Mrs Lowden —

That evening —

THE END

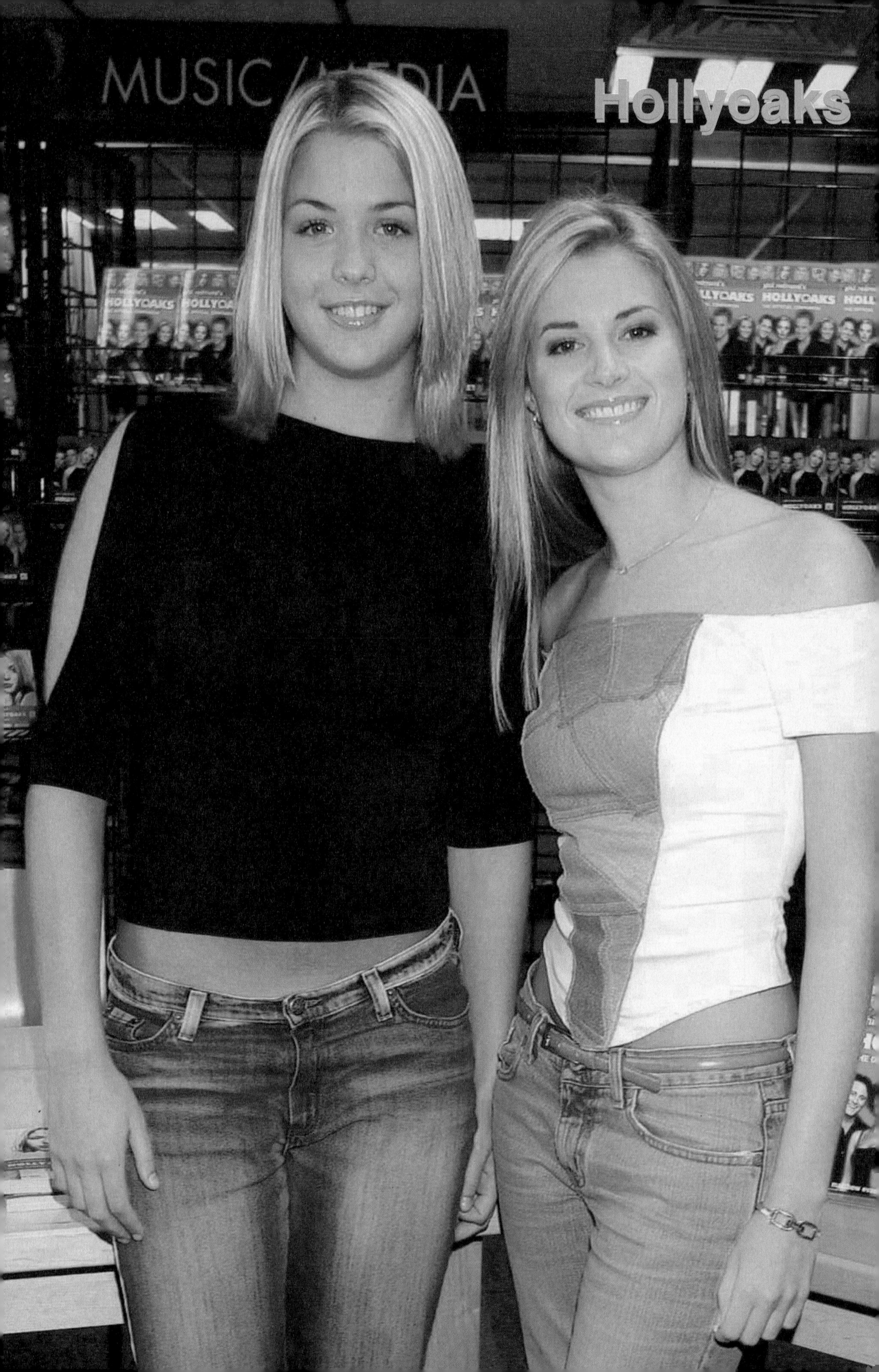
Hollyoaks
HOLLYOAKS

The laundrette's the ideal soap spot for Dot in EastEnders.

SOAPY STUFF!

Mad about TV soaps? Here are some facts you may *not* know about your favourite programmes.

Soaps - or Soap Operas as they were originally known - got their name because the first radio shows of this kind were sponsored by soap powder companies.

Lots of actors turn up in more than one soap. Nicola Duffett was Debbie in EastEnders before becoming Cat in Family Affairs.

Brookside, which began on 2nd November 1982, bought six real houses to use as a set.

Neighbours, our favourite Australian soap, was first shown in Britain in 1986.

Coronation Street is Britain's longest running TV soap.

The real name of Neighbours' Ramsay Street is Pin-Oak Court and the working title of the show was One Way Street.

Libby from One Way Street just wouldn't sound the same.

Can you tell Cat from Debbie?

Animal soap stars are hired from agencies - just like human actors.

It's a dog's life for animal actors!

Hollyoaks was devised by Phil Redmond - who also created Grange Hill and Brookside.

Emmerdale was originally called Emmerdale Farm. It began in 1972 with the funeral of Jacob Sugden.

Most drinks in soap bars are made from water and burnt sugar - but beer is sometimes real.

EastEnders was first shown at 7 o'clock on the 19th February, 1985, and began with the death of a man called Reg Cox.

Is the beer in the Coronation Street pub real - or coloured water?

ROVERS RETURN INN

ARE YOU A SOAP

Now test your knowledge of TV soaps past
and present with our fun quiz.

1. What did Emma and Curly Watts
call their baby in Coronation Street?
- a) Barney
- b) Bartholomew
- c) Benjamin

2. Who left Brookside after her stay
in the Celebrity Big Brother house?
- a) Claire Sweeney
- b) Vanessa Feltz
- c) Anthea Turner

3. What was strange about
EastEnders' Frank Butcher's funeral?
- a) Nobody turned up
- b) Frank wasn't dead
- c) It was held in a circus tent

4. What kind of animals appeared in
lots of commercial breaks during
Emmerdale?
- a) Gerbils
- b) Horses
- c) Dogs

5. In Home and Away, Zac Drayson
played which character?
- a) Duncan
- b) Will
- c) Vinnie

6. In Hollyoaks, what
relation is Abbie to Ben?
- a) Girlfriend
- b) Mum
- c) Sister

7. What were the names of Arthur and
Pauline Fowler's children in EastEnders?
- a) Mike, Martha and Morris
- b) Mo, Mandy and Milly
- c) Mark, Michelle and Martin

QUEEN?

8. Which famous Australian pop princess was **Spinning Around** years after she left **Neighbours**?

a) Kylie Minogue
b) Nicole Kidman
c) Dame Edna Everage

9. What did the Morgans name their cafe in **Hollyoaks**?

a) Central Perk
b) Deva
c) Cafe Nervosa

10. Which **Brookside** character suffered bullying?

a) Anthony Murray
b) Tim O'Leary
c) Jimmy Corkhill

ANSWERS: 1.c, 2.a, 3.a, 4.c, 5.b, 6.c, 7.c, 8.a, 9.b, 10.a

BROOKSIDE CLOSE

How many did you get right?

1-3: Soap rating - a tiny little bubble
Oh, dear! You really don't watch soaps, do you? But, hey, you have a fun-filled life without them!
You prefer real-life situations to the ones on TV.

4-6: Soap rating - quite frothy
Not a bad score. You only watch a few of the soaps and are selective. That's the way you are about lots of things, isn't it?

7-10: Soap rating - loadsa bubbles
You're a soap queen! You love the twists and turns of the plots and you sometimes turn on the drama yourself - but not for long!

Make...make...make.

For a different look this
Christmas, try making your own decorations!
Everything here is simple to make –
and doesn't cost much either. Have fun!

Merry Christmas

It's A Cracker!

Take an old cardboard
tube and a
piece of pretty
Christmas
paper which
is about twice
as long as the
roll, and wide enough to
wrap all the way round. Place
the tube in the centre of the paper and roll the paper round,
sticking it together with a little glue where it meets. Use pretty
matching or contrasting ribbon to tie the paper together at both
ends of the roll, but be careful not to tear the paper.

These crackers look great sitting
on window ledges,
or underneath the tree.

Tip
Why not use your
crackers as pretty
wrapping for small
presents? Place a
gift inside the roll
then make the
cracker as above.

Tinsel Twisters!

Buy a packet of Tinsel Stems from a craft shop and have **hours** of fun. Twist the stems together to make all kinds of fabby deccies - large and small. It's best to work on a covered surface, though, cos the tinsel can make quite a mess.

We've used a mix of colours to make stars, flowers and other shapes, but you can do whatever you like.

Tip
You can tie these to the branches of your tree with glitter thread or string. When they catch the light the deccies look just as sparkly as tree lights.

Poptastic!

String popcorn together to make a chain to drape round your Christmas tree or hang in your bedroom window. All you need is some salted popcorn (toffee or butter would be too sticky), a large needle and some glitter string or thread. Pick large pieces of corn – and be gentle, as the corn can crumble if you are too rough when threading it.

Tip
Make your chain extra special by tying coloured bows between some of the pieces of popcorn.

Have a cool Yule!

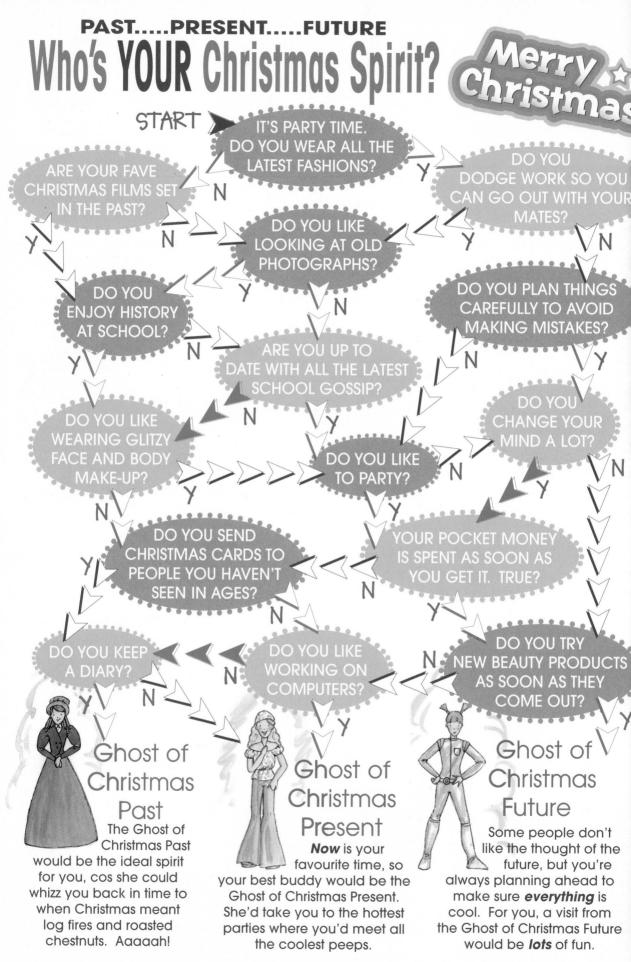

PAST.....PRESENT.....FUTURE

Who's YOUR Christmas Spirit?

Merry Christmas

START

IT'S PARTY TIME. DO YOU WEAR ALL THE LATEST FASHIONS?

ARE YOUR FAVE CHRISTMAS FILMS SET IN THE PAST?

DO YOU DODGE WORK SO YOU CAN GO OUT WITH YOUR MATES?

DO YOU LIKE LOOKING AT OLD PHOTOGRAPHS?

DO YOU ENJOY HISTORY AT SCHOOL?

DO YOU PLAN THINGS CAREFULLY TO AVOID MAKING MISTAKES?

ARE YOU UP TO DATE WITH ALL THE LATEST SCHOOL GOSSIP?

DO YOU CHANGE YOUR MIND A LOT?

DO YOU LIKE WEARING GLITZY FACE AND BODY MAKE-UP?

DO YOU LIKE TO PARTY?

DO YOU SEND CHRISTMAS CARDS TO PEOPLE YOU HAVEN'T SEEN IN AGES?

YOUR POCKET MONEY IS SPENT AS SOON AS YOU GET IT. TRUE?

DO YOU KEEP A DIARY?

DO YOU LIKE WORKING ON COMPUTERS?

DO YOU TRY NEW BEAUTY PRODUCTS AS SOON AS THEY COME OUT?

Ghost of Christmas Past
The Ghost of Christmas Past would be the ideal spirit for you, cos she could whizz you back in time to when Christmas meant log fires and roasted chestnuts. Aaaaah!

Ghost of Christmas Present
Now is your favourite time, so your best buddy would be the Ghost of Christmas Present. She'd take you to the hottest parties where you'd meet all the coolest peeps.

Ghost of Christmas Future
Some people don't like the thought of the future, but you're always planning ahead to make sure *everything* is cool. For you, a visit from the Ghost of Christmas Future would be *lots* of fun.

Merry Christmas

IT was two weeks before the end of the Christmas term, and "Grim Gertie" Grimstyle had news —

The Comp

AS YOU KNOW, EACH YEAR AT CHRISTMAS REDVALE COMPREHENSIVE PUTS ON A CONCERT FOR THE LOCAL OLD FOLKS. THIS YEAR, IT HAS BEEN DECIDED THAT THE THIRD AND FOURTH YEARS SHALL PROVIDE THE ENTERTAINMENT.

HEY, BRILLIANT!

WE'LL DO OUR NEW ACT, EH, FREDDY!

WHAT NEW ACT? WHAT'RE YOU ON ABOUT, HODGE?

HAVE TO WAIT AND SEE. WON'T YOU!

I BET HODGE AND FREDDY HAVEN'T EVEN GOT AN ACT. NOW THEY'LL HAVE TO THINK OF SOMETHING.

I'LL SING SOME NICE TRADITIONAL SONGS. MY MUM SAYS THAT'S WHAT OLD PEOPLE LIKE.

TRUST 'MY MUM SAYS' MARGARET TO COME UP WITH THAT!

WHY DON'T WE FOUR DO A DANCE ROUTINE?

GREAT IDEA, ROZ! LET'S LOOK OUT SOME MUSIC RIGHT NOW.

I CAN'T, BECKY. MY COUSIN SUZIE'S COMING TO STAY. I'VE GOT TO GO STRAIGHT HOME.

I THOUGHT I'D MET ALL YOUR COUSINS, LAURA. WHO'S SUZIE?

I HAVEN'T SEEN HER FOR YEARS. HER MUM'S GOING INTO HOSPITAL SO SHE'S STAYING WITH US UP TILL CHRISTMAS. SHE USED TO BE DEAD SHY.

So —

I'VE EMPTIED TWO DRAWERS AND HALF THE WARDROBE FOR YOU, SUZIE. NEED ANY HELP UNPACKING?

NO, THANKS, LAURA. IT'S REALLY GOOD OF YOU TO MOVE ALL YOUR STUFF FOR ME.

And —

WHAT'S SHE LIKE, THEN?

DEAD QUIET, HAYLEY. SHE SPENT MOST OF THE EVENING IN OUR ROOM WITH A BOOK. IT'LL BE DIFFERENT ON MONDAY, THOUGH.

HOW COME?

HER MUM DOESN'T WANT HER TO MISS SCHOOL, SO SHE'S SPENDING THE LAST FEW DAYS OF TERM AT THE COMP, WITH US.

GEE, THAT'S TOUGH! SHE MUST'VE BEEN HOPING SHE'D HAVE AN EXTRA-LONG CHRISTMAS HOLIDAY!

At Laura's —

IT'S GREAT NEWS ABOUT YOUR MUM DOING SO WELL IN HOSPITAL, SUZIE.

DO YOU WANT TO JOIN OUR DANCE TEAM?

OH, NO! I CAN'T DANCE. I — I'LL JUST WATCH.

ONE TWO THREE, TURN. FIVE SIX SEVEN, KICK!

SUZIE SEEMS TO LIKE IT. SHAME SHE CAN'T DANCE.

On Monday —

LIKE A CRISP, SUZIE?

THIS WAY FOR THE GUIDED TOUR OF THE TORTURE CHAMBER!

CLAIRE AND NIKKI AND EVERYONE ARE BEING REALLY NICE TO SUZIE, BUT SHE JUST SMILES. I'VE NEVER KNOWN ANYONE SO MOUSY!

In art —

IT'S FINISHED — SOOTY COLE'S IN FOR A SURPRISE!

YEAH — CAN'T WAIT TO SEE HIS FACE!

WHAT ARE THOSE TWO UP TO?

IT'S HENRY, THE SCHOOL SKELETON!

LATER WE'LL ASK SOOTY FOR SOMETHING FROM THE CUPBOARD.

But —

AH, MR COLE. COULD I HAVE A BOX OF PENCILS, PLEASE?

CERTAINLY, MISS GRIMSTYLE. HELP YOURSELF FROM THE CUPBOARD.

OH, NO!

EEEAGH!

WHOSE STUPID, CHILDISH IDEA OF A JOKE IS THIS?

ER — AHEM! I'M SURE IT'S ALL IN FUN, MISS GRIMSTYLE. AFTER ALL, IT IS CHRISTMAS!

Mr Cole succeeded in calming her down —

HA, HA! DID YOU SEE GERTIE'S FACE?

IT WAS BRILLIANT!

EVEN BETTER THAN CATCHING SOOTY!

111

ALL RIGHT, DAVID HODGSON AND JOHN FREDERICKS! YOU'D BETTER PUT THAT SKELETON BACK IN THE SCIENCE LAB WHERE HE BELONGS — *WITHOUT* HIS SANTA SUIT. I'M CONFISCATING THAT TILL THE END OF TERM!

EH? HOW DID YOU KNOW IT WAS US?

SOOTY'S A GOOD SPORT. HE WAS STRUGGLING NOT TO LAUGH HIMSELF WHEN HE SAW GERTIE'S FACE!

SUZIE LAUGHED HER SOCKS OFF THEN. MAYBE SHE'S NOT SO SHY AND MOUSY AFTER ALL.

That night —

HEY — THAT SOUNDS LIKE OUR DANCE MUSIC. WHAT'S GOING ON? HAVE ROZ AND THE TWINS COME OVER WHILE I WAS IN THE LIBRARY?

SUZIE! SO *THAT'S* WHY SHE DIDN'T WANT TO COME TO THE LIBRARY WITH ME!

OH! L-LAURA. I — I DIDN'T KNOW YOU WERE THERE! I THOUGHT EVERYONE WAS OUT.

BUT THAT WAS BRILLIANT, SUZIE. YOU'VE LEARNED NEARLY EVERY STEP OF OUR DANCE JUST FROM WATCHING US. GO ON!

NO, I C-CAN'T DANCE IF I KNOW ANYONE'S WATCHING. I FEEL STUPID.

BUT YOU'RE GOOD, SUZIE. YOU COULD EASILY DANCE WITH US!

SUZIE'S WATCHED US EVERY TIME WE'VE REHEARSED — IT'S LIKE SHE REALLY *DOES* WANT TO JOIN IN, BUT . . .

HAYLEY? WHAT'S UP?

OH, MY KNEE'S A BIT SORE NOW . . .

And, after lunch —

LAURA — BAD NEWS. HAYLEY'S KNEE'S REALLY SWOLLEN AND SORE AFTER ALL OUR DANCING. THERE'S NO WAY SHE CAN DANCE!

WHAT? BUT THE CONCERT'S TOMORROW!

SUZIE, WILL YOU HELP US OUT?

TAKE HAYLEY'S PLACE? *NO!* I TOLD YOU — I CAN'T! YOU CAN DO THE DANCE WITH JUST THE THREE OF YOU. *PLEASE*, LAURA!

WE *CAN'T!* YOU KNOW IT HAS TO BE FOUR. PLEASE, SUZIE — FOR MY SAKE? IT'S ONLY IN OUR SCHOOL HALL AND IT'S FOR A GOOD CAUSE!

WELL, I — I'LL TRY. BUT I KNOW I'LL BE TERRIBLE.

But —

WOW! SUZIE REALLY *CAN* DO OUR DANCE!

YOU KEEP THIS UP, SUZIE, AND IT WON'T BE HODGE AND FREDDY WHO ARE THE STARS OF THE SHOW!

Next day —

I — I SHOULD N-NEVER HAVE SAID I'D DO IT. I C-CAN'T. I FEEL S-SICK.

WE'VE ALL GOT BUTTERFLIES, SUZIE. IT'S NATURAL! LET'S GO TO THE WINGS AND WATCH THE OTHER ACTS. 'MY MUM SAYS' MARGARET'S ON!

♪ OH, DON'T DECEIVE ME, OH NEVER LEAVE ME . . . ♪

MARGARET'S GOT A NICE VOICE, I SUPPOSE — EVEN IF HER SONGS ARE A BIT BORING. STILL, THE OLD FOLKS SEEM TO LIKE THEM.

TA-DAAA! AND NOW — PRESENTING — THE GREAT FREDERICO!

SO THAT'S THEIR BIG SECRET — A MAGIC ACT! THIS SHOULD BE A LAUGH.

MY ASSISTANT TEARS THE PAPER INTO A THOUSAND PIECES AND TIPS IT INTO THE HAT.

. . . AND, HEY PRESTO, THE PAPER IS WHOLE AGAIN.

SEE . . . OH!

IT WORKED BEFORE!

HA, HA, HA, HA!

AHEM! FOR MY NEXT TRICK — THE AMAZING SOLID WATER! I TURN THE GLASS UPSIDE DOWN, REMOVE THE CARD — AND THE WATER . . .

. . . STAYS IN THE GLASS. OO-ER!

GLUB!

HO, HO, HO!

I'M TELLING YOU, THOSE TRICKS ALL WORKED BEFORE! THE GIRLS PUT ME OFF.

THAT'S THE LAST TIME I DO A MAGIC ACT WITH *YOU*, MATE!

THE 'GREAT' FREDERICO. HA, HA, HA!

Then it was the girls' turn —

SUZIE'S DOING REALLY WELL. AND THE AUDIENCE IS STARTING TO CLAP ALONG.

YOU LOT WERE GREAT!

IT WAS FUN! I STOPPED FEELING SICK AS SOON AS I WAS UP THERE. AND I *DID* IT, DIDN'T I? I DANCED IN FRONT OF ALL THOSE PEOPLE!

YOU SURE DID, SUZIE! YOU KNOW, YOU SHOULD TAKE UP DANCING.

I'D LIKE THAT, ROZ!

I DON'T THINK MY COUSIN WILL BE QUITE SO SHY IN FUTURE. THANKS TO YOU, HAYLEY!

ME? WHY ME?

I JUST WONDERED HOW BAD YOUR LEG WAS. I MEAN, WHEN YOU WALKED IN JUST NOW YOU'D LOST YOUR LIMP, BANDAGE OR NO BANDAGE!

AHEM! WELL! WE HAD TO SEE IF YOU WERE RIGHT ABOUT SUZIE, DIDN'T WE? AND YOU WERE!

HEY, EVERYONE — LOOK AT SOOTY COLE!

OUR SANTA SUIT! SO *THAT'S* WHY HE CONFISCATED IT!

YOU HAVE TO ADMIT IT, HODGE — HE SUITS IT A LOT BETTER THAN HENRY DID! HA, HA!

THE END

THE GIFT

A Touch Of Christmas Magic For You!

Jenny peered through her window and shivered with delight. Eleven o'clock on Christmas Eve, and it had just started to snow.

Beyond her garden stood the old housing estate. Most of the people had moved out but, even although it was dark, Jenny could clearly see the house where Stacy and her mum lived - and someone was sitting on an old chair by the garden shed. With a shock, Jenny realised it was Stacy, wearing pyjamas and a thin coat, snow dressing her hair like sequins.

It's nearly midnight, Jenny thought, anxiously. Why isn't Stacy tucked up in bed?

Outside Jenny pushed aside the broken fence, and tramped across the untidy garden.

"Stacy?" Jenny whispered, crouching beside the little girl who sat, looking pinched with cold. "It's late and it's freezing. Why aren't you in bed?"

"I'm waiting for Santa Claus," Stacy replied, wiping snowflakes from her eyes.

Jenny smiled to herself as she gently hugged Stacy.

"If you're not asleep by the time Santa comes, he won't leave you anything," she explained, gently.

"He never leaves me anything, anyway," Stacy replied. "So I'm waiting to make sure he doesn't miss me again."

Jenny suddenly ached inside. She knew Stacy's mum didn't have much money, but didn't realise Stacy never got any Christmas presents. She bit her lip. "What will you ask for?"

"You know that jewellery shop opposite the chemist in the precinct?" Jenny nodded. "Well, there are these diamond hair slides." Stacy stroked her long, chestnut hair. "They're beautiful, Jenny."

Jenny felt a lump in her

sight. Jenny smiled as she looked around her. A white Christmas! Magic! And Stacy would have a gift. Not much of a gift - but a gift nevertheless

Then, as she reached the shed, Jenny stopped short.

There on Stacy's chair lay a shiny red box. Jenny moved closer. A gift tag poked from beneath a silver bow. "To Stacy, with love." No name.

Carefully Jenny lifted the lid and there, snuggled in a red velvet nest, were two of the most beautiful jewelled hair slides she had ever seen. Someone else must have known Stacy wanted those slides. But who?

SOMETHING MADE JENNY LOOK UP ...

Then, as Jenny tucked her old slides in her pocket and turned to go home, she noticed the footprints leading through the snow to Stacy's gift. Only *one* set of prints. Her own. So how had someone else reached the chair to leave the gift? If they'd walked through the garden, they'd have left a trail.

Jenny scanned the snow around her for signs of a visitor, but the snow lay crisp and deep and undisturbed. Then, suddenly, something made her look up towards the snow-laden sky.

Was that bright light a falling star – or a comet shooting through the night?

Jenny held her breath as a strange sound drifted towards her. It was the sound of distant laughter.

---

throat. "Santa can't always get us what we want," she said softly.

Stacy nodded. "Anything would do really. I just want Santa to remember me."

Jenny stared at the young child. Her lips were turning mauve, and her thin coat was getting very wet. "Come on, Stacy," she said, urging the little girl towards the house. "Get dry and go to bed. Santa will visit you tonight, I'm sure of it. Come to this chair in the morning and see what you find."

CHRISTMAS SHOULD BE MAGICAL ...

When Jenny got home, she sat by the fire and thought hard. She wanted to make sure Stacy got at least one present this Christmas. Christmas should be magical for children, so there was no way

Jenny wanted Stacy's dreams to be shattered again. She closed her eyes tightly and tried to think.

Moments later, she was rifling through drawers in the spare bedroom. She scrabbled through boxes and small bags until she found what she was looking for - a grubby, faded box. Jenny removed the lid and stared inside. Two hair slides lay on a bed of white foam. The stones were dull with age, and the settings were a bit tarnished, but they'd have to do.

Racing downstairs, Jenny ran some soapy water into a bowl and washed the slides. They still didn't look like new, but they looked brighter. Jenny put them in their box, replaced the lid, and found some wrapping paper.

By the time Jenny had slipped back outside, the snow had formed a thick blanket over everything in

The Four Marys

Merry Christmas

MARY RADLEIGH

MARY COTTER

MARY FIELD

MARY SIMPSON

IT was the week before Christmas and at St Elmo's School for Girls, preparations were well under way for the end of the term.

THAT LOOKS GREAT, SUSIE. WHAT ABOUT THE 'PRESENTS', LAURA?

HERE THEY ARE!

DUMMY PARCELS! WHAT A STUPID IDEA! IMAGINE PUTTING MARY FIELD IN CHARGE OF DECORATIONS!

MABEL WOULD HAVE BEEN *MUCH* BETTER. YOUR IDEAS ARE *SOOO* OLD-FASHIONED.

THEY'RE *SUPPOSED* TO BE. I WANT A TRADITIONAL LOOK.

BORING MORE LIKE!

HOLLY, YOUR LADYSHIP!

IN THAT CORNER, SERF — AND QUICKLY!

HA, HA, HA! I'M GLAD I'M NOT *REALLY* YOUR SERVANT, FIELDY.

121

Soon it was time for the draw —

FIRST TO DRAW IS SUSIE. REMEMBER — DON'T SAY WHO YOU'VE CHOSEN.

But —

OH! I'VE PICKED MY OWN NAME!

OOPS! YOU CAN'T BUY *YOURSELF* A SECRET PRESENT! JUST PUT IT BACK AND YOU CAN DRAW AGAIN.

Everything went well, and soon —

ONLY ME LEFT TO DRAW NOW. REMEMBER, ALL PRESENTS MUST BE UNDER THE TREE BY TUESDAY NIGHT.

I WISH I KNEW WHO PICKED ME.

WELL I HOPE MABEL DIDN'T DRAW *MY* NAME!

That evening —

I'LL SEE IF THERE'S ANYTHING SUITABLE IN THIS CATALOGUE.

I KNOW *EXACTLY* WHAT *I'M* GOING TO GET.

D'YOU THINK MRS MITCHELL WOULD PREFER SHOWER GEL OR BUBBLE BATH?

COTTY! YOU'RE NOT SUPPOSED TO TELL WHO YOU'RE BUYING FOR!

WE WON'T TELL ANYONE, BUT I THINK SHOWER GEL WOULD BE BEST. *I'M* BUYING CHOCOLATE FUDGE.

WORDS, W[O

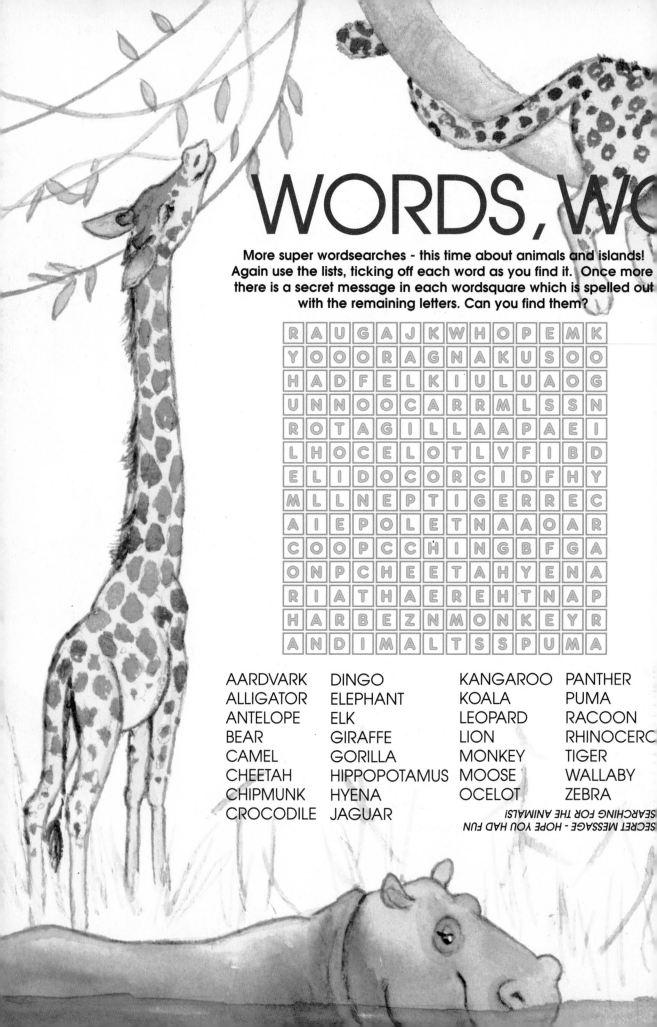

More super wordsearches - this time about animals and islands!
Again use the lists, ticking off each word as you find it. Once more
there is a secret message in each wordsquare which is spelled out
with the remaining letters. Can you find them?

R	A	U	G	A	J	K	W	H	O	P	E	M	K
Y	O	O	O	R	A	G	N	A	K	U	S	O	O
H	A	D	F	E	L	K	I	U	L	U	A	O	G
U	N	N	O	O	C	A	R	R	M	L	S	S	N
R	O	T	A	G	I	L	L	A	A	P	A	E	I
L	H	O	C	E	L	O	T	L	V	F	I	B	D
E	L	I	D	O	C	O	R	C	I	D	F	H	Y
M	L	L	N	E	P	T	I	G	E	R	R	E	C
A	I	E	P	O	L	E	T	N	A	A	O	A	R
C	O	O	P	C	C	H	I	N	G	B	F	G	A
O	N	P	C	H	E	E	T	A	H	Y	E	N	A
R	I	A	T	H	A	E	R	E	H	T	N	A	P
H	A	R	B	E	Z	N	M	O	N	K	E	Y	R
A	N	D	I	M	A	L	T	S	S	P	U	M	A

AARDVARK	DINGO	KANGAROO	PANTHER
ALLIGATOR	ELEPHANT	KOALA	PUMA
ANTELOPE	ELK	LEOPARD	RACOON
BEAR	GIRAFFE	LION	RHINOCER[O
CAMEL	GORILLA	MONKEY	TIGER
CHEETAH	HIPPOPOTAMUS	MOOSE	WALLABY
CHIPMUNK	HYENA	OCELOT	ZEBRA
CROCODILE	JAGUAR		

SECRET MESSAGE - HOPE YOU HAD FUN
SEARCHING FOR THE ANIMALS!